Schoolhouse Phonics
Level C

CONTENTS

Say each picture name. Write the letter that stands for the beginning consonant sound to complete each word.

1. <u>b</u>ed

2. ___ap

3. ___an

4. ___ing

5. ___et

6. ___all

7. ___oap

8. ___op

9. ___ug

10. ___ub

11. ___at

12. ___ose

13. ___ix

14. ___en

15. ___ike

16. ___ug

Initial consonants **s**, **m**, **t**, **p**, **n**, **r**, **b**, and **j**

Say each picture name. Write the letter that stands for the ending
consonant sound to complete each word.

1. cu_p_	**2.** su_n_	**3.** ca_r_	**4.** ba_t_
5. nur_s_e	**6.** ha_m_	**7.** ca_p_	**8.** cu_d_
9. ja_r_	**10.** pea_ch_	**11.** we_d_	**12.** ne_t_
13. fa_n_	**14.** ca_d_	**15.** bea_r_	**16.** bu_s_

4 Unit 1/Lesson 1

Final consonants **s, m, t, p, n, r,** and **b**

Say each picture name. Write the letter that stands for the beginning consonant sound to complete each word.

1. d og

2. f ish

3. W ag

4. v an

5. z oo

6. y ard

7. h and

8. l eg

9. h ose

10. W ell

11. K iss

12. l id

13. K ite

14. f ire

15. y arn

16. d oll

Say each picture name. Write the letter that stands for the ending consonant sound to complete each word.

1. lea f

2. ca___e

3. bo___

4. snee___e

5. be___

6. fi___e

7. sa___

8. sea___

9. boo___

10. a___

11. pai___

12. hi___e

13. bea___

14. roo___

15. hee___

16. hoo___

Say each picture name. Write the letter that stands for the consonant sound you hear in the middle of the word.

1. v	**2.** ___	**3.** ___	**4.** ___
5. ___	**6.** ___	**7.** ___	**8.** ___
9. ___	**10.** ___	**11.** ___	**12.** ___
13. ___	**14.** ___	**15.** ___	**16.** ___

Medial consonants **d, b, l, t, m, p, r, v, z, g,** and **n**

Say each picture name. Write the letter that stands for the consonant sound you hear in the middle of the word to complete each word.

1. chim_n_ey	**2.** spi__er	**3.** pi__ot	**4.** le__on
5. ti__er	**6.** ra__io	**7.** bea__er	**8.** leo__ard
9. me__er	**10.** wa__on	**11.** ra__or	**12.** sho__el
13. dra__on	**14.** ro__ot	**15.** mi__er	**16.** ru__er

Medial consonants **d, b, l, t, m, p, v, g,** and **n**

Say each picture name. Write the letters that stand for the beginning
and ending consonant sounds to complete each word.

1. h a m	2. __i__e	3. __ea__	4. __o__e
5. __e__	**6.** __a__	**7.** __ee__	**8.** __a__e
9. __a__	**10.** __ea__	**11.** __i__e	**12.** __e__
13. __o__e	**14.** __i__	**15.** __ai__	**16.** __ea__

Say each picture name. Write the missing consonant letters to
complete each word.

1. l e m o n

2. ___o___e

3. ___i___e

4. ___ea___u___

5. ___i___e

6. ___u___e___

7. ___e___e___

8. ___ea___

9. ___or___e

10. ___o___o___

11. ___o___e

12. ___a___o___

13. ___ea___e___

14. ___ea___

15. ___ea___

16. ___i___e___

When **c** is followed by **a, o,** or **u,** or is the last letter in a word, it usually has the hard sound, as in **cat.** When **c** is followed by **e, i,** or **y,** it usually has the soft sound, as in **city.** Say each picture name. Circle either **hard c** or **soft c** to show which sound of **c** the picture name has.

1.	2.	3.	4.
card	bracelet	cot	cart
(hard c) | soft c	hard c | soft c	hard c | soft c	hard c | soft c

5.	6.	7.	8.
ceiling	cymbals	city	fence
hard c | soft c	hard c | soft c	hard c | soft c	hard c | soft c

9.	10.	11.	12.
cap	cub	mice	vacuum
hard c | soft c	hard c | soft c	hard c | soft c	hard c | soft c

13.	14.	15.	16.
celery	cork	bacon	lilac
hard c | soft c	hard c | soft c	hard c | soft c	hard c | soft c

Hard and soft consonant **c**

When **g** is followed by **a, o,** or **u,** or is the last letter in a word, it usually has the hard sound, as in **goat.** When **g** is followed by **e, i,** or **y,** it usually has the soft sound, as in **gym.** Say each picture name. Circle either **hard g** or **soft g** to show which sound the picture name has.

1. gate	2. engine	3. huge	4. dragon
(hard g) soft g	hard g soft g	hard g soft g	hard g soft g

5. bug	6. giant	7. gum	8. cage
hard g soft g	hard g soft g	hard g soft g	hard g soft g

9. page	10. wagon	11. gem	12. giraffe
hard g soft g	hard g soft g	hard g soft g	hard g soft g

13. gorilla	14. goat	15. gym	16. bag
hard g soft g	hard g soft g	hard g soft g	hard g soft g

Hard and soft consonant **g**

Read the words in the box. Write each word under the correct heading.

cat	gem	wagon	pencil
goat	ceiling	gym	wage
music	mice	cute	rice
engine	huge	city	good
cone	game	fence	bag
rug	giant	cake	cuff

hard c

cat

soft c

hard g

soft g

Say each picture name. Write the missing consonant letters.

1. __a__o__	**2.** __a__	**3.** __i__o__	**4.** __oa__
5. __a__	**6.** __a__io	**7.** __i__e	**8.** __a__e
9. __o__	**10.** __a__e__	**11.** __a__e	**12.** __e__e__
13. __i__e	**14.** __e__e__	**15.** __a__y	**16.** __a__

When vowel **a** comes between two consonants, it has the short sound of **a,** as in **cat.** Say each picture name. Circle the word that names the picture.

1.	2.	3.	4.	5.
tab can tan (cab)	rat bag rag bat	pan hat tan pat	pad pat sad sat	tap tan map man
6.	7.	8.	9.	10.
jam ram cap rap	ran jab ram jam	sat bag bat sag	hat ham sat Sam	fat mat fan man

Read each sentence. Choose a circled word from above to complete each sentence. Then write the word on the line.

1. Jan sat on Dad's lap in the ____cab____.

2. Nan asked us not to eat all the _____.

3. Can you find Little Falls on the _____?

4. That old frying _____ does not look very clean.

5. The lambs and the _____ are in the pen.

6. Please carry the ham in the tan _____.

7. Sam put on the _____ because he was warm.

8. Susan will draw a picture on the _____ of paper.

9. Have Max clean the mat with a _____.

10. Should I buy the blue _____ or the tan one?

Say each picture name. Write the word that names the picture.

1.	2.	3.	4.	5.
__ham__	_____	_____	_____	_____
6.	7.	8.	9.	10.
_____	_____	_____	_____	_____

Read each sentence. Choose one of the words in the box to complete each sentence. Then write the word on the line.

1. The tan cat just ___had___ eight kittens.

2. Would you jump if you saw a flying _____?

3. Pam sat on my _____ in the van.

4. Did you know that a cap is a kind of _____?

5. Tim _____ visit you next Wednesday.

6. Ham that is not good tastes _____.

7. I felt _____ when my best friend moved away.

8. Nan _____ as fast as her dad.

9. Don't eat too much and you will not get _____.

10. After playing tag, little Dan must _____.

hat
sad
bat
lap
had
fat
can
nap
bad
ran

Short vowel **a**

When vowel **e** comes between two consonants, it has the short sound of **e**, as in **hen.** Say each picture name. Circle the word that names the picture.

1. men   pan
   met   pet

2. ten   Ben
   Meg   bet

3. red   jet
   led   met

4. hen   peg
   pen   beg

5. let   led
   wed   wet

6. wet   men
   den   web

7. ten   Ben
   bet   Peg

8. bet   beg
   leg   let

9. net   hen
   pet   hem

10. pen   pet
    net   red

Read each sentence. Choose a circled word from above to complete each sentence. Then write the word on the line.

1. Two ___men___ helped Dad move the piano.

2. Bev asked Mom to let her fly in a _____.

3. Jim fell down and hurt his _____.

4. Six vans plus four vans make _____ vans.

5. We caught eight butterflies in the _____.

6. Mom likes it when _____ helps her clean the den.

7. The old _____ does not write very well.

8. A fly is trapped in the spider _____.

9. The tan rag is too _____ to use.

10. That red _____ likes to sit by the fan!

Say each picture name. Write the word that names the picture.

1. hem	2.	3.	4.	5.
6.	7.	8.	9.	10.

Read each sentence. Choose one of the words in the box to complete each sentence. The write the word on the line.

1. Bev ___let___ us play with her pet cat.

2. My mom has not yet _____ Ted.

3. Eight jets plus two jets make _____ jets.

4. Please _____ the table for dinner.

5. Will you buy the blue pen or the _____ one?

6. Maria hopes to _____ a bike for her birthday.

7. The TV set is on in the _____.

8. What runs faster, a rat or a _____?

9. Peg _____ her cat some fish.

10. Did Ben see that show _____?

yet
ten
fed
let
set
den
met
red
get
hen

Short vowel e

Phonics in Action

Read the story.

Pals at Camp

Ken packs his bags and gets in the van. Then he is at camp. He gets to his tent and sees his pal Sam. Ken and Sam go to a craft class. Ken makes a red hat rack. Sam makes a bed for his pet cat.

When the pals get on a raft, they get wet. Then they swim laps. Sam rests. Ken has a nap.

Next, Ken will play tag with his pals. Sam will catch bugs with a net. The pals are glad to be at camp.

Write the word on the line that completes each sentence about the story.

1. Ken gets in a _____ to go to camp.

2. Ken and Sam go to a _____ class.

3. Sam will catch bugs with a _____.

REVIEW Short vowels **a** and **e**

Say the name of the picture as you slide down the hill. Print the name on the line. The first one shows you what to do.

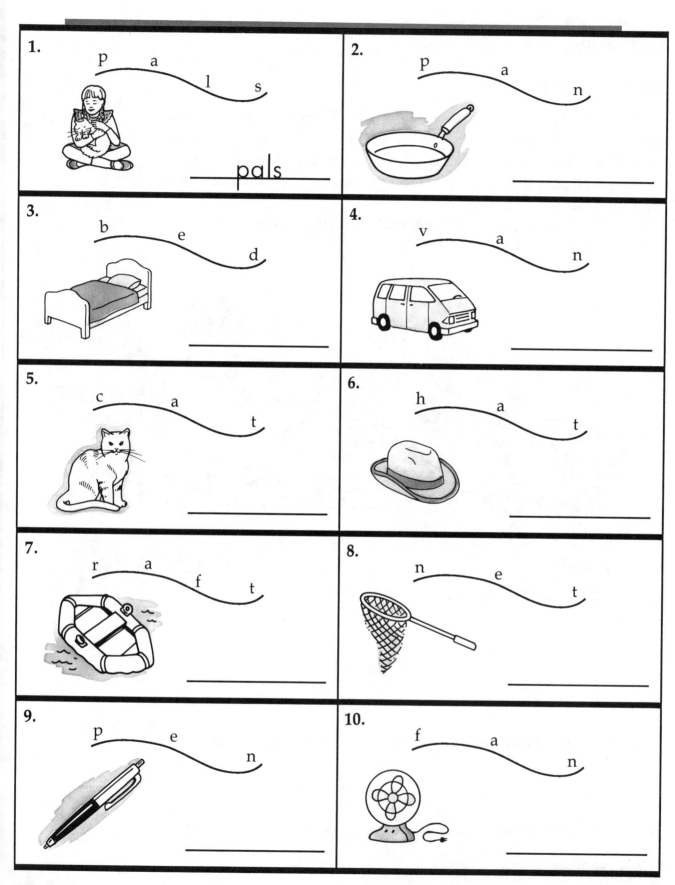

1. p   a   l   s

pals

2. p   a   n

_____

3. b   e   d

_____

4. v   a   n

_____

5. c   a   t

_____

6. h   a   t

_____

7. r   a   f   t

_____

8. n   e   t

_____

9. p   e   n

_____

10. f   a   n

_____

When vowel **o** comes between two consonants, it has the short sound of **o,** as in **fox.** Say each picture name. Circle the word that names the picture.

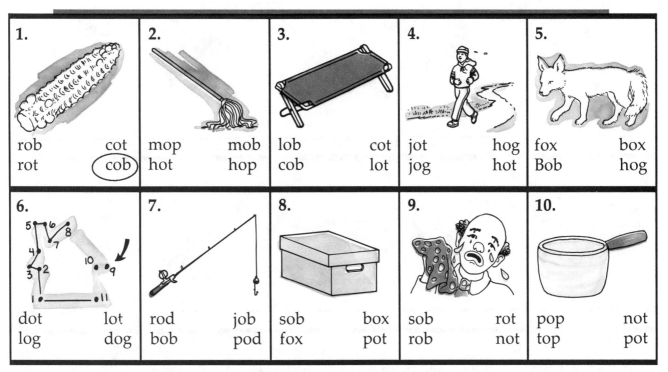

1.	2.	3.	4.	5.
rob cot rot (cob)	mop mob hot hop	lob cot cob lot	jot hog jog hot	fox box Bob hog
6.	7.	8.	9.	10.
dot lot log dog	rod job bob pod	sob box fox pot	sob rot rob not	pop not top pot

Read each sentence. Choose a circled word from above to complete each sentence. Then write the word on the line.

1. The pig eats every ___cob___ it sees.

2. Bob will take a nap on the _____.

3. Tom and his mom like to _____ together.

4. Use the tan pan, not the black _____.

5. Put a _____ at the top of the small **i** in **wish.**

6. Please put the old fan in the _____.

7. The clever _____ tricked the chickens.

8. You can clean up the den with a wet _____.

9. My dad gave me his old fishing _____.

10. Pete started to _____ when he saw the sad movie.

Short vowel **o**

Say each picture name. Write the word that names the picture.

1.	2.	3.	4.	5.
cob				

6.	7.	8.	9.	10.

Read each sentence. Choose one of the words in the box to complete each sentence. Then write the word on the line.

1. That tan _____pot_____ is too hot to pick up.

2. Ron likes to read about frogs with his _____.

3. Someone who is two or three is called a _____.

4. Do you like to eat ham that is _____ or cold?

5. The empty _____ is covered with tall weeds.

6. Dad is going to start his new _____ this fall.

7. If you keep the meat out, it may _____.

8. Sara _____ a new game for her birthday.

9. We ate a kind of fish called _____.

10. It is _____ going to rain on Saturday.

rot
got
hot
mom
pot
lot
tot
job
not
cod

Phonics in Action

Read the story.

Jan and Tom

Jan's dad went to see a band. Jan has Tom, the tot. Tom is sad to see Dad go. He sobs and yells. His neck gets red. Jan pats Tom on the back. Tom does not stop. Then Jan gets Tom's red and tan top. Tom is glad.

Now Tom has to be fed. Jan gets ham and corn on the cob for the tot. Tom tosses the ham. Jan steps on the mess. She gets a rag. Then Tom wants apple juice. Jan gets him a glass. Tom drops it. Jan gets the mop.

Jan gets Tom into bed. Tom hops and yells. Jan begs Tom to stop, but Tom does not. Jan gets the cat. Tom helps pet the cat. Tom nods off into a nap.

Dad gets home and asks about Tom. "He was a doll," says Jan. "I am glad when I can lend a hand."

Write the word on the line that completes each sentence about the story.

1. Tom sobs and _____ for his dad.

2. Jan _____ on Tom's ham.

3. Jan tells Dad that Tom was a _____.

NAME _____

Say the word that you make as you slide down the hill. Then circle the word. The first one shows you what to do.

1.
d   a   d

(dad)
glad
did
Dan

2.
n   o   t

got
hot
not
net

3.
s   o   b

cob
sob
set
mop

4.
r   a   g

rug
rag
rig
ran

5.
r   e   d

rod
fed
red
led

6.
m   o   p

mop
map
mom
cob

7.
h   a   m

Sam
ham
hum
gum

8.
f   e   d

led
fat
get
fed

9.
g   e   t

got
let
hit
get

10.
T   o   m

men
Jen
Ken
Tom

REVIEW Short vowels **a, e,** and **o**

NAME _____

When vowel **u** comes between two consonants, it has the short sound of **u**, as in **bug**. Say each picture name. Circle the word that names the picture.

1.	2.	3.	4.	5.
cub cup dug (bun)	jug tug hum mud	hut but tub rug	mug dug mud gum	us sun run nut

6.	7.	8.	9.	10.
rut bug rug but	mug but mud bud	pub pup cup cut	but us bus dug	hug hut jug tug

Read each sentence. Choose a circled word from above to complete each sentence. Then write the word on the line.

1. Would you like some ham on a ___bun___?

2. Sandy likes to _____ her new pup.

3. Peg is washing off the mud in the _____.

4. A cub is little and so is a _____.

5. Look for the mugs and the _____.

6. The _____ is a small rose.

7. A very hot drink is in that green _____.

8. The _____ gives light to the earth.

9. A cab is much smaller than a _____.

10. The new white _____ is in the den.

NAME _____

Say each picture name. Write the word that names the picture.

| 1. cub | 2. | 3. | 4. | 5. |

| 6. | 7. | 8. | 9. | 10. |

Read each sentence. Choose one of the words in the box to complete each sentence. Then write the word on the line.

1. José is going to ___run___ every morning.

2. I can _____ better than I can sing.

3. Please _____ Tracy a piece of cake.

4. Clean the _____ off the rug with a wet rag.

5. Jam is good to eat on a _____.

6. What is the _____ of ten plus five?

7. The cub's leg will get better if we _____ it.

8. I like the blue cap, _____ I like the red one better.

9. Dad gave me a _____ when I sat on his lap.

10. It would be _____ to play with Tom.

bun
mud
run
sum
fun
hum
but
hug
cut
rub

26 Unit 2/Lesson 12

Phonics in Action

Read the story.

The Job

Glen wants to spend time at camp. "I know it would be such fun to go with my pals. We could sleep in a tent," Glen tells his mom and dad. Glen's dad is sad. He wants to send Glen to camp, but camp costs a lot.

Glen runs to see his pal Stan. "How can I help?" Stan asks. Glen and Stan get a plan.

The pals go the the stand on the next block. They ask the man at the stand for a job. The man says yes. Glen gets a big box. He sells hot dogs and pop. Stan gets nuts in a cloth bag. He stands at the end of the block and yells. The pals get big bucks. Stan gets a tip!

Glen and Stan run to Glen's dad. They can help pay for camp. Glen's dad is glad. His mom gives the pals a big hug. Glen can go pack his bags. Glen and Stan will share a bunk!

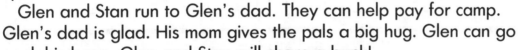

Write the word on the line that completes each sentence about the story.

1. Glen wants to go to _____.

2. Stan asks his pal Glen how he can _____.

3. Glen's mom gives Glen and Stan a _____.

Say the name of the picture as you slide down the hill. Print the name
on the line. The first one shows you what to do.

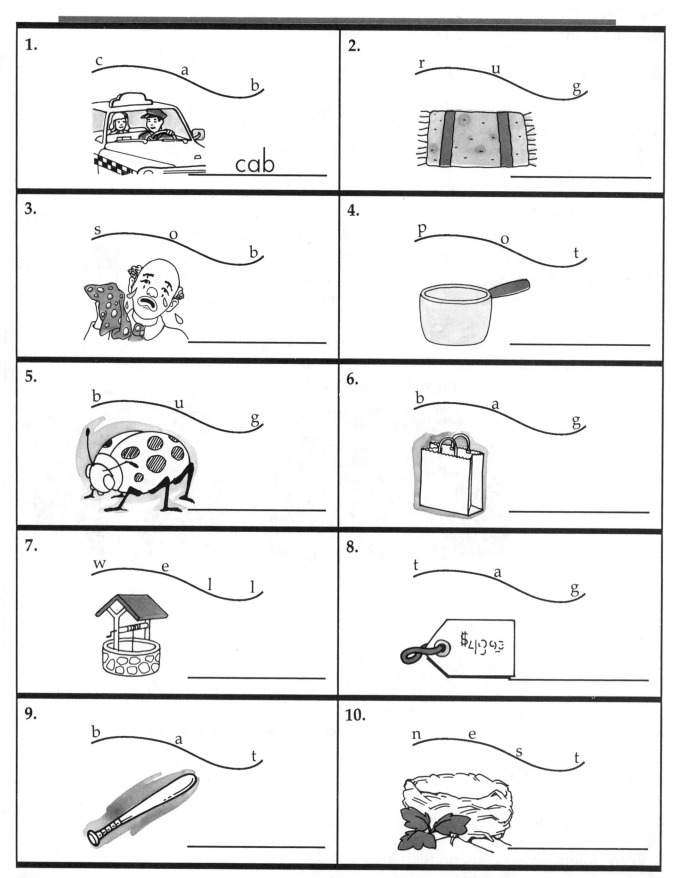

1. c a b
cab _____

2. r u g
_____

3. s o b
_____

4. p o t
_____

5. b u g
_____

6. b a g
_____

7. w e l l
_____

8. t a g
$4.99
_____

9. b a t
_____

10. n e s t
_____

REVIEW Short vowels **a, e, o,** and **u**

When vowel **i** comes between two consonants, it has the short sound of **i**, as in **pig.** Say each picture name. Circle the word that names the picture.

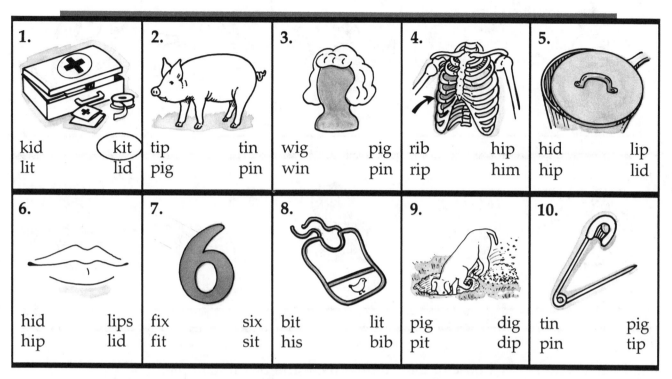

1.	2.	3.	4.	5.
kid (kit)	tip tin	wig pig	rib hip	hid lip
lit lid	pig pin	win pin	rip him	hip lid

6.	7.	8.	9.	10.
hid lips	fix six	bit lit	pig dig	tin pig
hip lid	fit sit	his bib	pit dip	pin tip

Read each sentence. Choose a circled word from above to complete each sentence. Then write the word on the line.

1. We can make a little jet with this ____kit____.

2. A fox would look funny in a red _____.

3. Little Jim will put on a _____ to keep clean.

4. Please fix the pot with the tin _____.

5. Can you help me _____ up the hem?

6. Dad was sad when he hurt his _____.

7. The tan pups have a lot of fun when they _____.

8. Do your _____ hurt when you bite them?

9. Look at the _____ roll in the mud.

10. Kim is five but soon she will be _____.

NAME _____

Say each picture name. Write the word that names the picture.

1. ___hip___	2. _____	3. _____	4. _____	5. _____
6. _____	7. _____	8. _____	9. _____	10. _____

Read each sentence. Choose one of the words in the box to complete each sentence. Then write the word on the line.

1. Who can ___rip___ this old rag in two?

2. Will you please _____ up Dan's coat?

3. Pat's job is to carry this _____ box.

4. Is your old hat small or does it _____?

5. Tim likes to read about dogs with _____ dad.

6. The light in here is too _____ to see.

7. Did Nan hurt a rib or her _____?

8. I can't see where the fox _____.

9. Dad said to ride in the van with _____.

10. Please pick up any _____ cans you see.

fit
him
zip
tin
rip
hid
big
his
dim
hip

Short vowel i

When vowel letters **ea** come between two consonants, they may have the short sound of **e,** as in **head.** Say each picture name. Circle the vowel letters that stand for the short sound of **e.**

| 1. w(ea)ther | 2. heavy | 3. bread | 4. bedspread | 5. lead |
| 6. head | 7. feather | 8. thread | 9. gingerbread | 10. breakfast |

Choose one of the words from above to complete each sentence. Write the word on the line.

1. Do you like it when the _____ weather _____ is warm or cold?

2. I can fix the rip with some _____.

3. Cookies made of _____ are my favorite.

4. Dad wants to eat two eggs for _____.

5. The hen looks funny with a hat on its _____.

6. Do you want any jam on your _____?

7. Bill's hat has a red _____ on the side.

8. Take off the _____ before you go to sleep.

9. The rocks were very _____ and hard to move.

10. Tina broke the _____ point of her pencil.

Read the three words in each box. Circle all three words if they rhyme.

1. (dread lead read)	**2.** thread threat spread	**3.** dead lard seed	**4.** leather wither rather
5. bread head red	**6.** feather weather heather	**7.** heavy heave leave	**8.** breath wreath teeth

Read each sentence. Circle the word that completes the sentence. Then write the word on the line.

1. Jan can see that the plant is _____dead_____. (dead) dad

2. Summer _____ is sunny and hot. **weather   mother**

3. Ben _____ the big test. **dreads   needs**

4. Sam wants to eat ham on _____. **bead   bread**

5. The big box was _____. **heavy   heady**

6. Dad put the new hat on his _____. **head   lead**

7. I will fix the sock if you get me the _____. **dread   thread**

8. Jan _____ that book last week. **red   read**

9. Mom will get a _____ for dad's hat. **feather   weather**

10. Put the _____ on the bed. **sped   spread**

Ea as short vowel e

Phonics in Action

Read the story.

The Big Trip

Lin and Gwen get a map and plan ahead. The pals will go to a land with lots of sun and sand. Gwen plans to swim in a vast sea of fish. Lin dreads the sea. She will not get wet. She will get a tan. She will stop at shops and go up paths.

The pals get set. Lin packs. She puts dresses on a rack. Gwen gets a hat with feathers. She puts it on her head. She picks up a fan to use in the hot sun.

Lin and Gwen get on a jet. The jet lifts off. It lands well. The pals get off and let a man help with their bags. Then they grin. Lin can go sit in the sun. She can get gifts for pals. Gwen can swim and have fun.

Write the word on the line that completes each sentence about the story.

1. Lin and Gwen get a _____ and plan ahead.

2. Lin _____ the sea.

3. Gwen plans to _____ in a vast sea of fish.

Read the sentence. Circle the word that rhymes with the underlined word. Write the word on the line.

1. It helps you get to new places. It rhymes with ca<u>p</u>. _____map_____

   sap
   mop
   (map)

2. You can dig in this at the beach. It rhymes with <u>land</u>. _____

   camp
   sand
   pond

3. You can do this at a mall. It rhymes with to<u>p</u>. _____

   shop
   trip
   ship

4. This goes on the floor. It rhymes with <u>mug</u>. _____

   run
   rag
   rug

5. It travels quickly. It rhymes with <u>set</u>. _____

   jog
   jet
   met

6. It lives in the sea. It rhymes with <u>wish</u>. _____

   wash
   fit
   fish

7. It makes a day cold or hot. It rhymes with <u>feather</u>. _____

   weather
   water
   father

8. It helps plants grow. It rhymes with <u>fun</u>. _____

   suds
   sun
   fin

9. You can do this in the sea. It rhymes with <u>dim</u>. _____

   slim
   swam
   swim

10. You put your hat on this. It rhymes with <u>spread</u>. _____

   heed
   deed
   head

REVIEW Short vowels **a, e, o, u, i,** and **ea**

Say each picture name. Write the word that names the picture.

1.	2.	3.	4.
_____	_____	_____	_____

5.	6.	7.	8.
_____	_____	_____	_____

9.	10.	11.	12.
_____	_____	_____	_____

13.	14.	15.	16.
_____	_____	_____	_____

TEST Short vowels **a, e, o, u, i,** and short vowel **e (ea)**   Unit 2/Lesson 17   **35**

Read each sentence. Choose one of the words in the box to complete
it. Then write the word on the line.

six	bread	rib	mug	dig	let
bad	hot	ten	sun	map	him
van	mop	lead	wet	job	bus

1. Dad may hurt a _____ if he falls from up there.

2. Joan will not _____ me see the show.

3. Put on the fan if you room is _____.

4. Clean up with some rags and a _____.

5. Please put some jam on this _____.

6. The rain made the grass _____.

7. We must walk because there is no gas in the _____.

8. Bob gets tan when he sits in the _____.

9. Five comes right before _____.

10. You cannot write with a pencil that has no _____.

11. Ted will drink from the glass, not the _____.

12. Kim cannot play tag because she has a _____ cold.

13. Those pups like to _____ .

14. Meg works from eight to _____ every night.

15. Can you find Los Angeles on this _____?

16. Maria got a _____ in a pet shop.

17. I like José and I want to play with _____.

18. Susan takes the _____ to work.

TEST Short vowels **a, e, o, u, i,** and short vowel **e (ea)**

When a word has two vowels, the first vowel often has the long sound and the second is silent, as in **hay, rain,** and **cape.** Circle the word that names the picture.

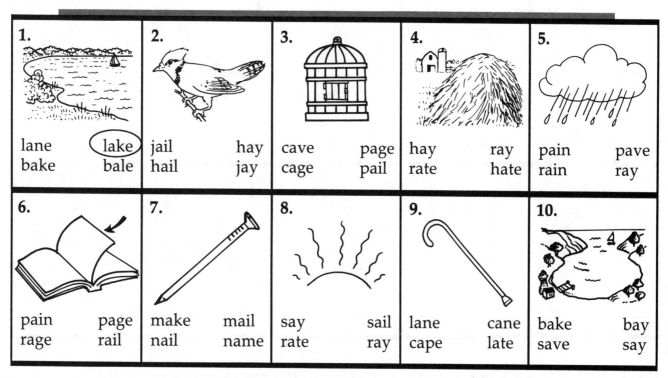

1.	2.	3.	4.	5.
lane (lake) bake bale	jail hay hail jay	cave page cage pail	hay ray rate hate	pain pave rain ray
6.	7.	8.	9.	10.
pain page rage rail	make mail nail name	say sail rate ray	lane cane cape late	bake bay save say

Read each sentence. Choose a circled word from above to complete each sentence. Then write the word on the line.

1. We can go sailing on the lake or ___bay___.

2. Did you see the blue _____ fly right onto Ray's head?

3. I will wash the van after I read this _____.

4. Put on your cape in case of _____.

5. Jane is using a _____ until her leg is better.

6. Mom can fix the old sandbox if she finds a _____.

7. If you look on the map, you will find the _____.

8. Look at the tan pups in the _____.

9. There is a big _____ of sun coming through the clouds.

10. Does a ram like to sleep in the _____?

Say each picture name. Write the word that names the picture.

1. __rail__

2. _____

3. _____

4. _____

5. _____

6. _____

7. _____

8. _____

9. _____

10. _____

Read each sentence. Choose one of the words in the box to complete each sentence. Then write the word on the line.

1. Buy some ____bait____ before you go to the lake.

2. Did Dad see the vase that Rosa _____?

3. Gail wants to fly a jet one _____.

4. Is the cab in the right _____?

5. Will it take long to _____ a ham?

6. I cannot _____ if I will be at the show.

7. You can pet the cub if it is _____.

8. Luis has a bad _____ in his leg.

9. What is the _____ of the new girl in class?

10. Does May Ling want to jog around the _____?

made
tame
bake
lake
pain
name
say
day
lane
bait

Long vowel **a**

When a word has two vowels, the first vowel often has the long sound and the second is silent, as in **bee** and **beak.** Circle the word that names the picture.

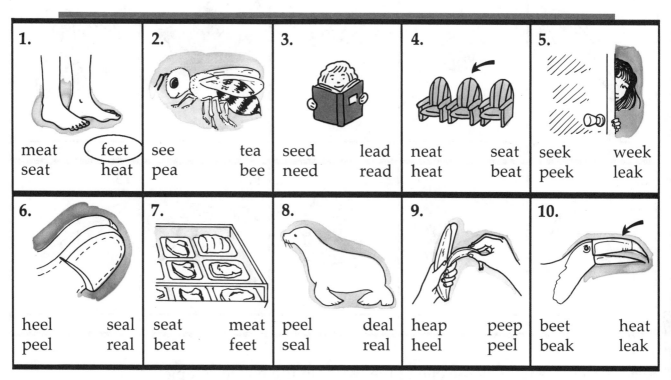

1.	2.	3.	4.	5.
meat (feet) seat heat	see tea pea bee	seed lead need read	neat seat heat beat	seek week peek leak

6.	7.	8.	9.	10.
heel seal peel real	seat meat beat feet	peel deal seal real	heap peep heel peel	beet heat beak leak

Read each sentence. Choose a circled word from above to complete each sentence. Then write the word on the line.

1. Don't walk on the rug if your ___feet___ are not clean.

2. Dad said not to _____ in the tan bag.

3. A yellow and black _____ is in the van.

4. Wash the mud off the _____ before you sit down.

5. Ham and beef are kinds of _____.

6. Pat cannot walk because her right _____ hurts.

7. I know you will laugh at the funny _____.

8. Kay likes to _____ about pets.

9. The blue jay does not have a big _____.

10. You can open the box if you _____ off the tape.

Say each picture name. Write the word that names the picture.

1. _pea_	**2.** _____	**3.** _____	**4.** _____	**5.** _____
6. _____	**7.** _____	**8.** _____	**9.** _____	**10.** _____

Read each sentence. Choose one of the words in the box to complete each sentence. Then write the word on the line.

1. Carla will ___need___ eight nails to fix the seat.

2. Kate and Jay like to _____ the funny ape.

3. Clean up the den so it looks _____.

4. When José and I raced, I _____ him.

5. Sam will drink _____ with his cookie.

6. Put on the heat if you _____ cold.

7. A bud will grow from that _____.

8. Eight of us are on the _____.

9. Will you eat beans or beets with your _____?

10. Linda wants to sail on the _____ some day.

seed
neat
feel
need
beat
team
feed
sea
tea
meal

Long vowel e

When a word has two vowels, the first vowel often has the long sound and the second is silent, as in **goat** and **rose**. Circle the word that names the picture.

1.	2.	3.	4.	5.
lobe lone (robe) rope	home hole role rode	boat bone coal coat	bone boat cone coat	nose note rose robe

6.	7.	8.	9.	10.
load rose road nose	coat goat vote boat	hope rope soap load	loaf load loan moan	hole coal coat vote

Read each sentence. Choose a circled word from above to complete each sentence. Then write the word on the line.

1. If there is no heat, you will need a ___robe___.

2. Don't ride the van over the _____ in the road.

3. The fox has a cold black _____.

4. Does a toad make a better pet than a _____?

5. That vase is too tall for the _____.

6. Will you put on the tan cape or the brown _____?

7. My dog will want to eat that big _____.

8. You will need to bake the _____ a little longer.

9. Please clean your face with _____ and water.

10. The cave has a lot of black _____ in it.

Long vowel **o**

Say each picture name. Write the word that names the picture.

1.	2.	3.	4.	5.
dome	_____	_____	_____	_____

6.	7.	8.	9.	10.
_____	_____	_____	_____	_____

Read each sentence. Choose one of the words in the box to complete each sentence. Then write the word on the line.

1. Maria hopes to get the ____role____ of Mrs. Krum in the play.

2. Jake and his mom _____ home in the bus.

3. The boat sailed all the way into the _____.

4. The little pup could not find its _____.

5. Do you know the _____ about the goat?

6. I hope Joan will _____ me her pretty beads.

7. Did you see that toad jump across the _____?

8. The little goat sleeps on a _____ of hay.

9. The team got only one _____ before the game was over.

10. Raul hopes no one will forget to _____.

cove
goal
role
load
vote
road
joke
loan
rode
home

Long vowel o

Phonics in Action

Read the story.

Bo and Lane Set a Goal

Bo and Lane like to row and sail. They like speedboats, too. The pals hope to take a day trip to a lake. They will go by rail. They need to raise cash for the train ride to the lake.

"I know!" says Bo. "We will get old clothes and junk. We will have a sale. Then we can pay for our ride to the lake."

Lane takes the old clothes and junk from home. They set up the sale on the grass. The two set a goal. Then Bo makes a note. Lane tapes a note to a pole. The sale is on!

Moms, dads, and pals go to the sale. Lane's mom gets beads and a hose. Bo's dad gets nails and a vase. A pal makes a deal for a robe. Bo and Lane make him a loan.

Bo and Lane sell all day. They keep the cash they make in a safe. They reach their goal. They will go on the train to the lake! The pals clean up. Then they grin and shake.

Write the word on the line that completes each sentence about the story.

1. Bo and Lane will take a trip to the _____.

2. Bo gets clothes and junk from _____.

3. Lane's mom gets _____ and a hose.

Read the clues for the puzzle. Then write the rhyming word in the correct place in the puzzle.

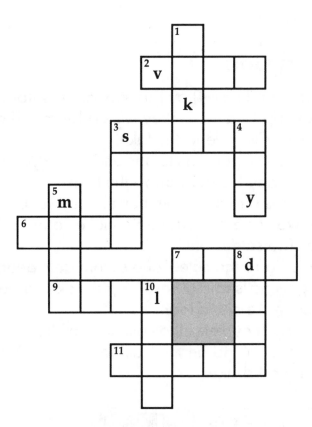

Across

2. You put flowers in it. It rhymes with <u>case</u>.
3. It means quickness. It rhymes with <u>reed</u>.
6. You can score this in hockey. It rhymes with <u>coal</u>.
7. You take this on a train or bus. It rhymes with <u>side</u>.
9. You hit this with a hammer. It rhymes with <u>tail</u>.
11. It lives in the sea. It rhymes with <u>pail</u>.

Down

1. You can swim in this water. It rhymes with <u>make</u>.
3. You do this on a boat. It rhymes with <u>tail</u>.
4. It is part of a week. It rhymes with <u>lay</u>.
5. It is a low cry. It rhymes with <u>cone</u>.
8. You can make a bargain. It rhymes with <u>meal</u>.
10. It is a name for a street. It rhymes with <u>cane</u>.

Long vowels **a**, **e**, and **o**

When a word has two vowels, the first vowel often has the long sound and the second is silent, as in **mule**. Circle the word that names the picture.

1.	2.	3.	4.	5.
rule (mule)	hug tub	rude fun	cone bus	cube tub
rug mug	huge tube	run fuse	cut boat	cub tube
6.	7.	8.	9.	10.
rude moan	cut hut	mug loan	dug dune	rub rug
rug mug	cute huge	lug moan	tune tug	tub tube

Read each sentence. Choose a circled word from above to complete each sentence. Then write the word on the line.

1. Does the _____mule_____ like beans or oats?

2. Do not let the tea bag soak too long in the _____.

3. Five of us walked on the _____.

4. A mule is big, but an elephant is _____.

5. There is not much paste left in the _____.

6. We have a new white _____ in our den.

7. Do you think a toad is _____?

8. A van is smaller than a _____.

9. Our lights went off when the _____ blew.

10. Sonia will find a _____ for her drink.

Say each picture name. Write the word that names the picture.

1. dune	2.	3.	4.	5.
6.	7.	8.	9.	10.

Read each sentence. Choose one of the words in the box to complete each sentence. Then write the word on the line.

1. Can you hum that funny little ___tune___?

2. If a hog is big, a mule is _____.

3. Little cubs and pups are so _____.

4. The two teams must play by every _____.

5. Sandy plays the _____ in the school band.

6. Many buds will start to show in May or _____.

7. They will not let huge dogs run on the _____.

8. It is _____ not to say please.

9. Please use a rag to clean the paint _____.

10. There is no way to fix the _____.

flute
cute
June
tune
rude
huge
rule
fuse
dune
tube

46   Unit 3/Lesson 22

Long vowel **u**

When a word has two vowels, the first vowel often has the long sound and the second is silent, as in **kite.** Circle the word that names the picture.

1.	2.	3.	4.	5.
fire (tire)	wire bite	dive five	Mike like	time hide
tile fine	kite fire	live hive	bike hike	lime dive
6.	7.	8.	9.	10.
bike like	dine fine	time dime	pine mine	nice rice
bite wide	nine line	lime vine	fine line	mice ride

Read each sentence. Choose a circled word from above to complete each sentence. Then write the word on the line.

1. Ms. Hoshida needs one new _____tire_____ for her van.

2. Eight bikes plus one bike make _____ bikes.

3. It is a great day to fly a _____.

4. A cub lives in a den and a bee lives in a _____.

5. My dad will hire _____ to rake the leaves.

6. Did you see the _____ run across the rug?

7. Pay the man a _____ for the lime.

8. Mom rides ten miles each day on her _____.

9. Please put the wet rags on the _____ outside.

10. Both a pea and a _____ are green.

Say each picture name. Write the word that names the picture.

1. dice
2. _____
3. _____
4. _____
5. _____

6. _____
7. _____
8. _____
9. _____
10. _____

Read each sentence. Choose one of the words in the box to complete each sentence. Then write the word on the line.

1. Is Mr. Lopez ____wise____ to dive into the lake?

2. The old mule cannot _____ the hay.

3. It was cold in the cave so we made a _____.

4. Are they toy mice, or are they _____ mice?

5. In a week or so, Kim is going on a _____.

6. Will Dad ride your bike or _____?

7. Five vines grow up the _____ of our home.

8. Was Jane late or on _____ for her new job?

9. It is one _____ from our home to the lake.

10. The mule eats oats and a small _____ of hay.

| mine |
| hike |
| mile |
| wise |
| fire |
| bite |
| pile |
| live |
| time |
| side |

Long vowel **i**

When **y** is at the end of a word, it can stand for the long sound of **i** as in **dry** or the long sound of **e** as in **pony.** Say each picture name.
Circle **long e** or **long i** to show the sound **y** stands for in each picture name.

1. pony	2. sky	3. why	4. army
(long e) long i	long e long i	long e long i	long e long i

5. jelly	6. cherry	7. penny	8. fry
long e long i	long e long i	long e long i	long e long i

9. dry	10. bunny	11. fly	12. twenty
long e long i	long e long i	long e long i	long e long i

13. city	14. shy	15. pry	16. baby
long e long i	long e long i	long e long i	long e long i

Y as long vowel **e** or **i**

Say each picture name. Circle the word that names the picture.

1.
happy
(heavy)
lobby

2.
hairy
dairy
fairy

3.
army
city
pony

4.
sly
spy
by

5.
penny
sunny
funny

6.
my
try
dry

7.
bunny
funny
sunny

8.
fairy
hairy
cherry

9.
thirty
jelly
heavy

10.
belly
jelly
silly

11.
city
pony
baby

12.
lobby
hobby
happy

13.
funny
sunny
cherry

14.
holly
jolly
hobby

15.
fry
dry
cry

16.
hobby
baby
thirty

Y as long vowel **e** or **i**

Read the words in the box. Write each word under the correct heading.

holly	fry	my	sly	every	pony
cry	penny	hurry	wry	shy	spy
happy	story	party	lady	body	heavy
dry	fly	why	by	sky	ply
sleepy	jelly	baby	bunny	pry	sty

long e

holly _____   _____

_____   _____

_____   _____

_____   _____

_____   _____

_____   _____

_____

long i

_____   _____

_____   _____

_____   _____

_____   _____

_____   _____

_____   _____

_____

Y as long vowel **e** or **i**

NAME _____

Read each sentence. Circle the word that completes the sentence. The write the word on the line.

1. ___Why___ don't you jog around the lake with us? (Why) Shy

2. Ben had tea and a bun with _____ for breakfast. **sunny jelly**

3. My dad will _____ to fix your bike today. **try why**

4. I saw many kinds of roses on our ride in the _____. **penny country**

5. Look at the huge jet in the _____. **dry sky**

6. Do you know the tale about a _____ called Peter? **bunny sunny**

7. We like to watch the blue jay _____ from tree to tree. **shy fly**

8. Shawn cannot lift that _____ suitcase. **berry heavy**

9. Save this dime and _____ to buy lunch. **penny funny**

10. Marc and Judy started to _____ at the sad movie. **my cry**

11. Linda will be _____ to show you where she works. **army happy**

12. Ten beads and ten beads make _____ beads. **twenty cherry**

13. The _____ crawled across the floor. **baby jelly**

14. We can get a free ride on a mule or a _____. **shiny pony**

15. Max knows how to tell a very _____ joke. **funny bunny**

16. Maria gave a bone to her new _____. **happy puppy**

17. The _____ lamb ran away from the little girl. **shy fry**

18. Ms. Wong rides in a van to her job in the _____. **berry city**

Y as long vowel **e** or **i**

Phonics in Action

Read the story.

A Happy Day

Jean's dad is not at home. He had to go away to a big job. He stays in a strange place. He misses Jean and her mom, so he sends them notes in the mail. Jean waits for the notes each day.

Jean writes to tell her dad that she is in a show. She will wear a fine dress. She will play a sweet tune on the flute. Her pal will play the lute.

The show is today. Jean will tape the show on a reel and mail the tape to her dad. Jean's mom drives in the sleet and snow. It is a long ride, but they get to the show. Jean goes on stage and plays. The teachers clap and tell Jean she is great.

Jean is very happy when she hears her name. She looks up. Her dad came to the show! This is the best day! Jean can only smile.

Write the word on the line that completes each sentence about the story.

1. Jean's dad went _____ to a big job.

2. Jean plans to mail a _____ of her show.

3. The teachers tell Jean she is _____.

REVIEW Long vowels **a, e, o, u, i,** and **y**

Read the sentence. Circle the word that rhymes with the underlined word. Write the word on the line.

1. It is the place you sleep. It rhymes with <u>dome</u>. ___home___

   heed
   cone
   (home)

2. You do this if you do not leave. It rhymes with <u>lay</u>. _____

   stay
   sty
   stalk

3. It means every one. It rhymes with <u>beach</u>. _____

   none
   each
   rack

4. It is something you send. It rhymes with <u>tail</u>. _____

   mall
   still
   mail

5. It is something to play. It rhymes with <u>hoot</u>. _____

   flute
   float
   fort

6. It is another word for *sob*. It rhymes with <u>shy</u>. _____

   say
   fly
   cry

7. You do this to make notes. It rhymes with <u>kite</u>. _____

   ride
   write
   wren

8. It is a cold rain. It rhymes with <u>meet</u>. _____

   sleet
   slit
   street

9. It means *good*. It rhymes with <u>line</u>. _____

   fire
   loan
   fine

10. It is part of a song. It rhymes with <u>dune</u>. _____

   dome
   tune
   cone

Say each picture name. Circle the letters that stand for the vowel
sound. Then write the letters on the line to complete the word.

1. oa / ai m____l	**2.** y / ay cit__	**3.** i-e / u-e l__n__	**4.** ie / oa b____t
5. oa / ai p____l	**6.** a-e / i-e r__k__	**7.** ie / y fl__	**8.** ea / oa l____f
9. u-e / a-e c__b__	**10.** ie / ea p____	**11.** u-e / o-e c__n__	**12.** ea / ie t____
13. ai / ee b____t	**14.** a-e / i-e d__v__	**15.** ei / oa c____ling	**16.** ay / ea h____

Read each sentence. Choose the word in the box that completes each sentence. Then write the word on the line.

week	soak	rain	sail	pie
tune	necktie	mice	cave	ceiling
fry	hose	vine	seats	

1. Do green peas grow on a _____?

2. Little Tony looked grown-up in his new _____.

3. Instead of cake, we ate _____.

4. My mom will _____ the boat around the bay.

5. Will you all please sit in your _____?

6. Sunday is the first day of the _____.

7. The firefighter uses a _____ to put out a fire.

8. Can we _____ the old rags in the tub?

9. I hope the cage of _____ will be safe.

10. Can Kay hum the _____ "Row, Row, Row Your Boat"?

11. My dad wants to _____ the meat in a deep pan.

12. The roses need _____ to grow.

13. We could not see the nine cubs in the _____.

14. A spider crawled up to the _____.

Say each picture name. Write the letters that stand for the beginning consonant blend.

1. <u>tr</u>umpet	**2.** _____og	**3.** _____ess	**4.** _____oom	**5.** _____actor
6. _____opeller	**7.** _____ide	**8.** _____ayon	**9.** _____aid	**10.** _____etzel

Use one of the consonant blends from above to complete the unfinished word in each sentence.

1. Kate won first ___pr___ize in the race.

2. Please put the mugs and pot of tea on a _____ay.

3. Do grapes grow on a vine or on a _____ee?

4. Grapes are a kind of _____uit.

5. Did Julio buy the tan coat or the _____ay one?

6. Please clean up the floor with a mop and a _____oom.

7. Did the first little pig make a home of hay or _____icks?

8. Mom put Greg's picture of his friends in a _____ame.

9. Do you want your _____ink in a cup or a glass?

10. My baby sister takes a nap in her _____ib.

Read each sentence. Choose one of the words in the box to complete it. Then write the word on the line.

brook	green	broil	train	drop	groom
crown	tracks	drum	brakes	prince	cream
print	free	cry	truck	frown	crowd

1. A jet is faster than a ____train____.

2. Beans and peas are _____.

3. Don't drive the truck if it has bad _____.

4. Weep means the same as _____.

5. Do we pay to cross the bridge, or is it _____?

6. The mug will break if you _____ it.

7. Tell the story of the frog that became a _____.

8. The king has a gold _____ on his head.

9. A van is smaller than a _____.

10. Mom drinks tea with _____ in it.

11. Craig plays a flute, not a _____.

12. We saw deer _____ in the snow.

13. Maria did not see her dad in the _____ of people.

14. Mrs. Taylor began to _____ when no one could answer her question.

15. Go across the bridge to get over the _____.

16. That big building is where they _____ the newspaper.

17. Fay is the bride and Mike is the _____.

18. Will Grandpa fry the meat or _____ it?

Initial consonant blends **fr, br, gr, cr, dr, pr,** and **tr**

Say each picture name. Write the letters that stand for the beginning consonant blend.

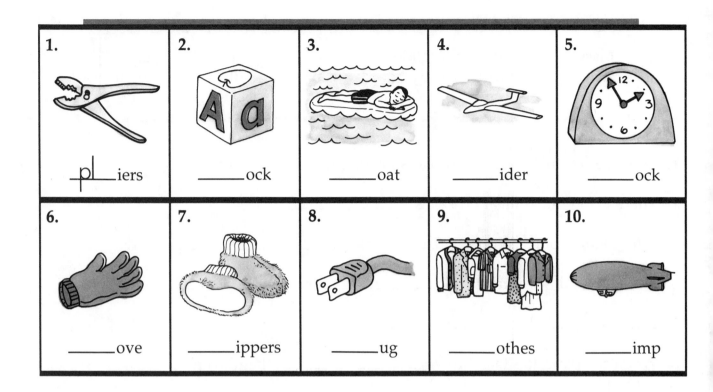

1. pl̲iers	**2.** _____ock	**3.** _____oat	**4.** _____ider	**5.** _____ock
6. _____ove	**7.** _____ippers	**8.** _____ug	**9.** _____othes	**10.** _____imp

Use one of the consonant blends from above to complete the unfinished word in each sentence.

1. The pony did not find a _____bl_____ade of grass to eat.

2. Can you find the United States on the _____obe?

3. Oats and beans are good crops to _____ant here.

4. A rose is a kind of _____ower.

5. Eight _____us one make nine.

6. Kim can fix the tray if she uses _____ue.

7. The _____own did a funny trick on a bike.

8. The plane was behind the big gray _____oud.

9. The truck could not _____imb the steep hill.

10. Dave wants jam on one _____ice of bread.

Read each sentence. Choose one of the words in the box to complete it. Then write the word on the line.

blast	floor	glide	plate	glad	bled
sled	club	fly	clay	flip	plain
slip	glare	plums	blade	clean	flute

1. The ____glare____ of the car's headlights hurt my eyes.

2. There is too much meat on Lisa's _____.

3. When Pam's pup won first prize, she was very _____.

4. Use soap and a wet rag to _____ the seats.

5. Eight dogs pulled the _____.

6. When the pancakes look brown, _____ them over.

7. Did you see the rocket _____ off into space?

8. Be careful not to _____ on the icy sidewalk.

9. José and Liza sing in the school _____.

10. The saw's _____ was too dull to cut the wood.

11. Bill played nine tunes on his _____.

12. Which do you like better, grapes or _____?

13. Does Miss Coyle's dress have any lace, or is it _____?

14. The playroom _____ is covered with tiles.

15. A toad is small, but a _____ is smaller.

16. Pop's lip _____ when he bit it.

17. Robin made a vase out of _____.

18. Did you see the paper plane _____ across the sky?

Say each picture name. Circle the letters that stand for the beginning consonant blend.

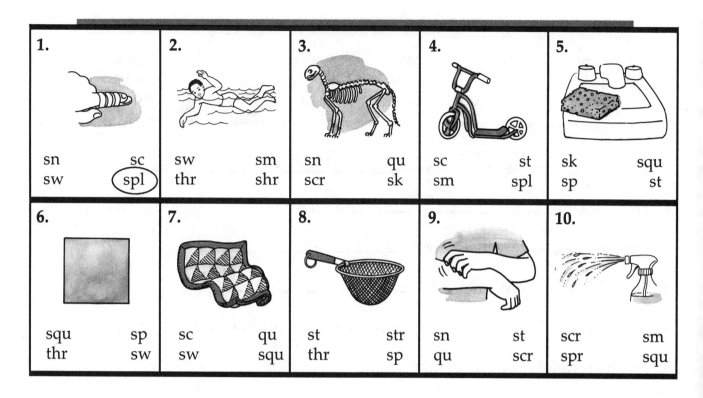

1.	**2.**	**3.**	**4.**	**5.**
sn sc	sw sm	sn qu	sc st	sk squ
sw (spl)	thr shr	scr sk	sm spl	sp st
6.	**7.**	**8.**	**9.**	**10.**
squ sp	sc qu	st str	sn st	scr sm
thr sw	sw squ	thr sp	qu scr	spr squ

Use one of the consonant blends from above to complete the unfinished word in each sentence.

1. If you spill the tea, it will ____st____ ain the rug.

2. A grin is the same as a big _____ ile.

3. Do flowers bloom in the _____ ing or fall?

4. Can five of us _____ eeze into your car?

5. A queen's chair is called a _____ one.

6. Can Sue dig the hole with a _____ ade?

7. When the lake freezes, we can _____ ate on it.

8. James and Patty raced their bikes down the _____ eet.

9. One kind of shellfish in the sea is _____ imp.

10. The children _____ eamed as the roller coaster went down.

Read each sentence. Choose one of the words in the box to complete it. Then write the word on the line.

snow	string	scale	sweet	scratch	spice
stick	scrub	skirt	strong	quiet	thread
smock	shrink	sprain	snail	squint	splash

1. The heat may cause the stamps to _____ stick _____ together.

2. This apple is _____ and juicy.

3. Can you help Gail hem her long _____?

4. Steve has blue paint all over his _____.

5. Tom will _____ the van to get off the mud and grime.

6. The man weighs the grapes on a _____.

7. Pepper is a _____ used to flavor food.

8. When the baby naps, we will be _____.

9. The bright sunlight may make you _____.

10. Mom hurt her finger but didn't _____ it.

11. Tie the big crate with some heavy _____.

12. We must leave before it begins to _____.

13. Wash the pants in cold water so they do not _____.

14. Dr. Green said not to _____ the mosquito bites on your arm.

15. You can mend the hole in the sweater with this _____.

16. The pups like to _____ in the tub.

17. You must be _____ to pick up this heavy box.

18. A clam is about the same size as a _____.

Say each picture name. Circle the letters that stand for the ending consonant blend.

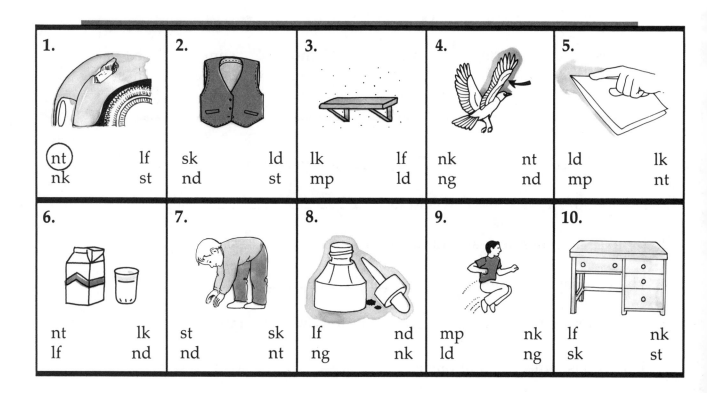

1.	2.	3.	4.	5.
(nt) lf	sk ld	lk lf	nk nt	ld lk
nk st	nd st	mp ld	ng nd	mp nt

6.	7.	8.	9.	10.
nt lk	st sk	lf nd	mp nk	lf nk
lf nd	nd nt	ng nk	ld ng	sk st

Use one of the consonant blends from above to complete the unfinished word in each sentence.

1. Marc cannot scrub the van all by himse___lf___.

2. You can mix red and white paint together to make pi_____ paint.

3. Mail cannot be sent without a sta_____.

4. Is there a cot or a sleeping bag in the te_____?

5. To bake a pie, the oven must be hot, not co_____.

6. Is it faster to skip or to wa_____?

7. Of all the coats, I like the green one be_____.

8. "Three Blind Mice" is the name of the song we sa_____.

9. The clothes on the line will dry in the wi_____.

10. Sweeping the floor is Robby's ta_____.

Final consonant blends **lf, mp, nt, st, nk, lk, sk, nd, ld,** and **ng**

Read each sentence. Choose one of the words in the box to complete it. Then write the word on the line.

rest	string	mask	lamp	sting	elf
wild	calf	silk	hand	drink	nest
dent	find	sink	plant	gold	talk

1. The van has a big _____dent_____ on the right side.

2. Do you know what the cow and its little _____ eat?

3. Brooke sat at her desk and turned on the _____.

4. The blue jay has four eggs in its _____.

5. Carmen likes to _____ her milk with a straw.

6. This cub is tame, but that one is _____.

7. Everyone at the party wore a funny _____.

8. When you opened Grandma's trunk, what did you _____?

9. You may use the pink soap next to the _____.

10. My baby brother cannot _____ yet.

11. Someday the bud will become a bean _____.

12. Ms. Chung put on her green beads and _____ bracelet.

13. Lie down on the cot if you need to _____.

14. The bee landed on Lee's leg but did not _____ him.

15. Bret holds the crayon with his right _____.

16. If you pull too hard, the _____ on the box will break.

17. My blouse is made of cotton, but my sister's blouse is made of _____.

18. Do you know the story about the funny little _____?

Phonics in Action

Read the story.

The Dream Queen

When Fran falls asleep, she has a great dream. She dreams she is a queen in the Land of Glee.

In the Land of Glee, it is always Spring. Plants and flowers grow up to the green sky. Blue trees produce huge pieces of fruit. Doves sing a sweet song as they fly. Monkeys swing in the trees and play. Children bask in the sun all day.

A spy in the Land of Glee slinks and creeps in the street. He makes the children cry. The moms and dads act grim. He is trying to take the queen away.

Fran can make the spy flee. She and a friend set a trap. They put the queen's hanky on a stick and hang it from the window. The spy slips in the window to steal Queen Fran. Her friend slams the window shut.

The spy is trapped. He screams and pleads to be set free. He claims he will quit spying and please the queen.

Queen Fran is just. She makes the spy clean and dust. The spy is glad. He will win the queen's trust.

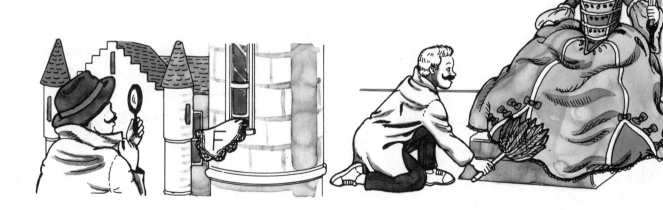

Write the word on the line that completes each sentence about the story.

1. Fran dreams that she is a _____.

2. A spy _____ and creeps in the street.

3. A friend helps to _____ the spy.

Say the word that you make as you slide down the hill. Then circle the word. The first one shows you what to do.

1.

v   e
        s   t

(vest)
vast
nest
net

2.

m   i
      l   k

malt
silk
milk
mill

3.

s   p
      y

spy
shy
spat
spit

4.

s   k   u
      n   k

spunk
spank
skunk
slink

5.

h   a
    n   d

band
Hank
sand
hand

6.

d   u
    s   t

dust
dirt
must
trust

7.

F   r
    a   n

fan
flan
Fran
Frank

8.

d   e
    s   k

rest
risk
desk
dusk

9.

c   r   u
    s   t

trust
trick
crust
slick

10.

w   i
    n   d

wand
sand
wink
wind

Read each sentence. Circle the letters that complete the unfinished word in the sentence. Then write the letters on the line.

1. The _____umpet made a lot of noise and woke us. **tr dr cr**

2. Kelly tied the _____aid in her hair with a ribbon. **gr br bl**

3. The old plane had a _____opeller that did not work. **tr cl pr**

4. The _____oom did not want to be late for his wedding. **pr br gr**

5. Joe likes to _____oat in the lake on hot days. **bl fl cr**

6. The big old _____ilt on the bed keeps me warm. **qu sm sc**

7. Sandy saw the hands on the _____ock move slowly. **bl cl cr**

8. The _____og in the pond croaked all day. **pr fr str**

9. My sister feeds table _____aps to the dog. **scr str spr**

10. My friends and I did many _____its in a few moments. **sl sk fl**

11. Sue ju_____ed when she heard her dad's voice. **nd mp st**

12. Mack lit the la_____ so he could read in bed. **nk st mp**

13. The bird had a broken wi_____. **st ll ng**

14. We went camping and saw many kinds of wi_____bears. **ld lk ng**

15. On weekends, Jack _____ends his cash at the mall. **bl sp cr**

16. If we are lucky, we will get cake and mi_____ today. **nd lk ng**

17. Fran cannot fi_____ her new dress in her room. **pr nd lk**

18. The new home is made of wood and _____icks. **sl fl br**

19. Mom almost cried about the de_____ in her new car. **mp nk nt**

20. The dog brings his master a pair of _____ippers. **fl st sl**

Read each sentence. Choose one of the words in the box to complete
it. Then write the word on the line.

split	screen	shrimp	slam	sneeze	sand
camp	storm	clean	flea	quack	past
throat	swan	trunk	bank	crop	sport

1. The _____ we had last night caused a lot of damage.

2. A bug that bites and has no wings is a _____.

3. Tracy could not talk because she had a sore _____.

4. You can broil or fry the _____ for dinner.

5. Golf is one _____ Mrs. Brown plays well.

6. Does an elephant drink with its _____?

7. The _____ on the window keeps bugs out.

8. The dust in our home makes Dad _____.

9. Once a week Fran puts money in the _____.

10. A grain of _____ is very small.

11. We need an ax to _____ the log.

12. Does a pup, calf, or duckling say _____?

13. Wipe off the desk with a _____ rag.

14. A pretty _____ swims in this stream.

15. Can you plant a _____ if the land is frozen?

16. Maria swims and plays tennis at _____.

17. The van drove _____ Ken's street.

18. Please don't _____ the gate when you close it.

TEST Initial and final consonant blends

When two consonants stand for one sound, the sound is called a consonant digraph, as in **sh**ip, **th**ick, **ch**in, **ph**oto, and **wh**ale. Say each picture name. Write the letters that stand for the beginning consonant digraph.

1.	2.	3.	4.	5.
th ermometer	____in	____ell	____otographer	____alk

6.	7.	8.	9.	10.
____ip	____oe	____umb	____armacy	____istle

Use one of the consonant digraphs from above to complete the unfinished word in each sentence.

1. I ____th____ink Carlos has a birthday this week.

2. Mr. and Mrs. Chen sailed to London on a huge _____ip.

3. Sarah put a _____erry on top of each cupcake.

4. Mom said I could have my own _____one in my bedroom.

5. The _____ite dog jumped up to catch the stick.

6. The big oak tree gives a lot of _____ade.

7. Fred saw a _____oto of his mom when she was six.

8. How many feet are _____ere in a mile?

9. Alicia likes to eat _____eese with an apple.

10. Kelly needs to fix the _____eels on her bike.

When two consonants stand for one sound, the sound is called a
consonant digraph, as in fi**sh**, wi**th**, pea**ch**, and gra**ph**. Say each
picture name. Write the letters that stand for the ending consonant digraph.

| 1. | 2. | 3. | 4. | 5. |
| phonogra_ph_ | too____ | ben____ | fi____ | por____ |

| 6. | 7. | 8. | 9. | 10. |
| mou____ | photogra____ | bru____ | pea____ | bu____ |

Use one of the consonant digraphs from above to complete the
unfinished word in each sentence.

1. This gra___ph___ shows the cookie sales for each day last week.

2. I wi_____ I could fly a jet.

3. The pup was clean after its ba_____.

4. Ann had meat, peas, and rice for lun_____.

5. Wanda will write a paragra_____ about her pet skunk.

6. The mo_____ landed on the lamp shade.

7. Luis helped his dad wa_____ the cups.

8. On hot days, I like to go to the bea_____.

9. I saw a dime on the pa_____ to Fran's home.

10. Please put the sliced ham on the serving di_____.

Read the story. Circle the words that begin or end with one of the
following: **sh, th, ch, ph,** or **wh.** Then write each word under the correct heading.

Today is moving day. My mom has a new job in New York and we want to live close to her work.

To get ready for our move, I helped my mom pack all our (things.) First I wrapped every dish, cup, pot, and pan and put them in a big box. Then I placed my phonograph in a box and made sure it would not move. While I was packing, my friend from next door came by and I gave him some games we could not take along. Before he left, Tomás helped me put our couch, table, and TV set on the porch.

"What else do I have to do?" I asked. My mom thought about it for a while. Then she told me to pack my suits, shirts, and shoes in a chest. My friend Ellen phoned in the afternoon to see if I needed any help. I thanked her and said I was doing fine. "Ellen," I asked, "will you come to see me in New York very soon?" Ellen said she would come in March.

After the chat with Ellen, I put the photos I took of our trip to Philadelphia in a safe place. Then my aunt and uncle came to say good-bye. After they left, I helped my mom clean the rooms. I felt sad about leaving. I had lived in our house a long time and would miss it. I looked around one last time. When I went outside to wait for the van, I felt uneasy but I did not know why. "I know!" I said. "My pet fish is still inside!"

sh	wh	ch

ph	th
	things

Read each sentence. Choose one of the words in the box to complete
it. Then write the word on the line.

teeth	phone	whistle	chewed	graph	with
shine	church	dish	thin	photo	phonograph
whiskers	thank	flash	peach	chore	shoes

1. The little white _____church_____ is just down the road.

2. We saw a _____ of lightning and then it started to rain.

3. Ali wants to buy a new pair of running _____.

4. The seal's _____ are very long and black.

5. The _____ showed my dad riding on a mule.

6. Chico got two new front _____ when he was seven.

7. The puppy _____ a hole in my slipper.

8. Please _____ Ms. Shane for the pretty roses.

9. Lisa wants to use the _____ to call her sister in Washington.

10. It is much too late to play the _____.

11. Mr. Ruiz showed us how to draw a bar _____.

12. When I _____, the blue jay comes out of its birdhouse.

13. If you clean the pot well, it will _____.

14. The _____ will be ripe in a day or two.

15. The roast beef is on the blue serving _____.

16. My _____ is to feed the cat every day.

17. Do you like to eat beans mixed _____ rice?

18. My pup was once fat, but now he is _____.

Initial and final consonant digraphs

When two consonants stand for one sound, the sound is called a consonant digraph, as in **wr**ite, **kn**ow, and **gn**at. Say each picture name. Write the letters that stand for the beginning consonant digraph.

1. ___gn___u	**2.** _____ench	**3.** _____ot	**4.** _____ight	**5.** _____ome
6. _____en	**7.** _____ob	**8.** _____ecker	**9.** _____it	**10.** _____ing

Use one of the consonant digraphs from above to complete the unfinished word in each sentence.

1. In the fairy tale, the ___gn___ome lives in a cave.

2. I don't want to fall and hurt my _____ist.

3. You will need a _____ife to slice the bread.

4. Iris fixed her bike with a _____ench.

5. Stan had to _____eel down to look for the pin.

6. A tiny bug that bites is a _____at.

7. I will use my new pen to _____ite a note.

8. Kim would like to _____ow more about apes.

9. We heard a loud _____ock at the door.

10. Dad will _____ap all the gifts on Sunday.

Say each picture name. Circle the letters that stand for the ending
consonant digraph. Then write the letters on the line to complete the word.

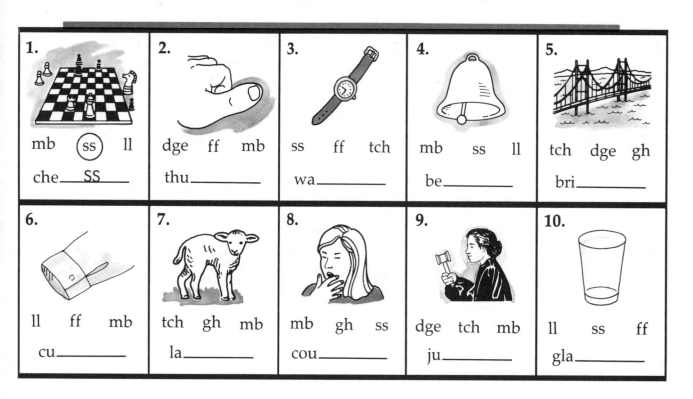

1. mb (ss) ll	2. dge ff mb	3. ss ff tch	4. mb ss ll	5. tch dge gh
che___SS___	thu_____	wa_____	be_____	bri_____
6. ll ff mb	7. tch gh mb	8. mb gh ss	9. dge tch mb	10. ll ss ff
cu_____	la_____	cou_____	ju_____	gla_____

Use one of the consonant digraphs from above to complete the
unfinished word in each sentence.

1. Tina earned a Girl Scout ba___dge___ for camping.

2. My cat can cli_____ to the top of the oak tree.

3. Lynn has a pretty pa_____ on her jeans.

4. I hope I don't mi_____ my favorite TV show.

5. Put all your stu_____ in the tan bag.

6. The funny joke made me lau_____.

7. Dan wants to se_____ iced tea on hot days.

8. My dad will help us clean this me_____.

9. The beach is just over the next ri_____.

10. My big sister used to co_____ my hair before I went to bed.

Final consonant digraphs **mb, ss, ll, ff, tch, dge,** and **gh**

NAME

Say each picture name. Look at the letters that stand for the consonant digraph in the word. Write the consonant digraph on the first, middle, or last line under the picture to show where it is heard in the word. Then write the word on the line.

1. ph	2. th	3. ch	4. th
ABCDEFGHI JKLMNOPQR STUVWXYZ			
___ ph ___	___ ___ ___	___ ___ ___	___ ___ ___

5. tch	6. ph	7. th	8. ch
___ ___ ___	___ ___ ___	___ ___ ___	___ ___ ___

9. sh	10. tch	11. ph	12. th
___ ___ ___	___ ___ ___	___ ___ ___	___ ___ ___

13. tch	14. sh	15. ch	16. tch
___ ___ ___	___ ___ ___	___ ___ ___	___ ___ ___

Medial consonant digraphs **sh**, **th**, **ch**, **ph**, and **tch**

Say each picture name. Write the letters that stand for the middle consonant digraph.

1. wi _sh_ bone	**2.** ba_____tub	**3.** ker_____ief	**4.** tele_____one	**5.** pi_____er
6. mo_____er	**7.** por_____es	**8.** bu_____es	**9.** wa_____es	**10.** dol_____in

Read each sentence. Circle the word that completes each sentence. Then write the word on the line.

1. Did the same _____author_____ write both stories? (author) alphabet

2. Rosa _____ her bike once a week. **inches washes**

3. Dad made both our _____ today. **lunches brushes**

4. The clown took a ride on the _____ back. **moth's elephant's**

5. Is the _____ nice or rainy? **weather marching**

6. The first one up at bat is the _____. **alphabet catcher**

7. We sent a code in dots and _____. **couches dashes**

8. Are these _____ ripe yet? **peaches galoshes**

9. It is easy to say the _____. **ditches alphabet**

10. The pots and pans are in the _____. **kitchen telephone**

Medial consonant digraphs **sh, th, ch, ph,** and **tch**

Phonics in Action

Read the story.

The Wish Game

Steph and Chet were at the beach. After lunch, their father said, "Your mother and I will stretch out on the sand and rest. You children can search for shells."

Steph and Chet went off to play at the water's edge. On the way, Chet heard a tiny cough. The children peeked behind a bush and saw a tiny gnome, no bigger than Chet's thumb. The gnome sneezed.

"Bless you!" said Steph.

The gnome looked up. "On, no! Don't come near me! If you will leave me alone, I will grant each of you a wish."

"It's a deal!" yelled Chet.

Steph wished for a ship to sail around the world. Chet wished for riches to share with his friends. In a blinding flash, a toy ship appeared at the shore, loaded down with shiny shells. The children turned to thank the gnome, but he was gone. As Steph and Chet turned to leave, they thought they heard a tiny cough!

Write the word on the line that completes each sentence about the story.

1. Chet heard a tiny _____ that came from a gnome.

2. The gnome will grant each child a _____.

3. Steph wished for a _____ to sail.

REVIEW Initial, medial, and final consonant digraphs

Read the clues for the puzzle. Then write the word in the correct place
in the puzzle.

Across

2. It connects two pieces of land. It rhymes with the name *Midge.*
4. It means *not smooth.* It rhymes with *tough.*
7. These are the little hairs on a cat's face.
8. It is another word for *stores.*
9. It helps you tell the time.
12. You can get it with jam for breakfast or make a sandwich with it for lunch.
14. It is like an elf. It rhymes with *comb.*
16. It is one of five fingers. It rhymes with *gum.*
17. Dogs do this to cats, and cats do this to mice.
18. It is a board game. It rhymes with *dress.*

Down

1. It is our planet. It rhymes with *mirth.*
3. You put food on this. It is another name for *plate.*
4. It means *hurry.* It rhymes with *gush.*
5. It is a type of chart. It rhymes with *staff.*
6. It is a long word for a snapshot.
7. It remains after a chicken dinner. It rhymes with *fish cone.*
9. It is a household tool. It rhymes with *French.*
10. It is in a mouth. When a baby one is lost, a new one grows.
11. You fix your hair with this. It rhymes with *gnome.*
13. You do this when something is funny.
15. This person runs a court. It rhymes with *budge.*

REVIEW Initial, medial, and final consonant digraphs

Read each sentence. Circle the letters that complete the word. Then write the letters on the line.

1. The baby made a fu_____ when we fed him strained beets. **ss ll gn**

2. Melanie got herself a cherry milk_____ake. **tch sh gh**

3. Mike's sister _____ows how to play cat's cradle. **kn gn ch**

4. Please _____one me if you need a ride home. **ff ph sh**

5. _____ere did you grow up? **Th Ph Wh**

6. I will not te_____ you what is inside the box. **ff ll ph**

7. Let's play catch with Jim and _____il. **Wr Ph Gn**

8. I hope this new trick will make you lau_____. **gh ph kn**

9. We rode to the coast to watch _____ales. **tch wh sh**

10. The rabbit will do_____ out of the way. **ph gn dge**

11. The workers put the sick man on the stre_____er. **tch gh sh**

12. When the boat docked, we came a_____ore. **ch ph sh**

13. Can you put this new _____eel on my bike? **wh gn kn**

14. That beaver will _____aw right through the tree. **gn kn wr**

15. My father's gloves are made of fine lea_____er. **sh th dge**

16. I mi_____ my big sister, who is away at school. **ll sh ss**

17. My coach will wa_____ me dive. **sh tch dge**

18. The _____ildren went to play in the park. **gn dge ch**

19. Stephanie sat on the cou_____ and read. **sh ch gh**

20. Lin had a runny nose and a cou_____. **sh ch gh**

Read each sentence. Write the consonant digraph that completes each unfinished word.

1. The ballplayer will sign her autogra_____ for me.

2. You will find the hoe and rake in the _____ed.

3. The _____ale lives in a huge tank at the zoo.

4. Everyone stood up when the ju_____ walked into the courtroom.

5. Carlos has been very sad since his dog's dea_____.

6. To dry the wet rag, _____ing it out.

7. The iced tea is in the tan pi_____er.

8. Push the tack into the wall with your thu_____.

9. The blue jay sat on a bran_____ of the tree.

10. Jill had a gold _____ain around her neck.

11. If you need aid, just ye_____.

12. My mo_____er just got a new job at the bank.

13. Kevin has a bad pain in his right _____ee.

14. Be careful not to ride your bike into the di_____.

15. Do you know how to play the game of che_____?

16. The sea is not safe when it is rou_____.

17. We saw the play in a big _____eater.

18. They spoke on the tele_____one last week.

19. I paid for my coat with ca_____.

20. The Cranes have many _____otos of their new baby.

TEST Initial, medial, and final consonant digraphs

When the vowel **a** or **o** is followed by the letter **r,** the vowel sound is neither long nor short. It is the vowel sound you hear in the words **car** and **corn.** Say each picture name. Circle the word that names the picture.

1.	2.	3.	4.
shore sharp short (shark)	hard horn born park	port part porch park	dart port pork dark
5.	**6.**	**7.**	**8.**
torn scarf thorn stork	barn arm army art	quart port part park	fort harp fork farm
9.	**10.**	**11.**	**12.**
cart cord card car	stork store start tore	cord cart card cork	army yarn scarf scar
13.	**14.**	**15.**	**16.**
card cork cart core	torch yarn yard tore	star shark horse scar	core bore torch torn

Read each sentence. Circle the word that completes the sentence. Then write the word on the line.

1. A chin and cheeks are ___parts___ of the face. **carts** (**parts**)

2. My goat sleeps on a pile of hay in the _____. **barn   bark**

3. Two kinds of meat are beef and _____. **stork   pork**

4. Four tires are needed for the brown _____. **car   jar**

5. We rushed inside before the _____ started. **form   storm**

6. Peas are green and _____ is yellow. **born   corn**

7. Mark can play the flute and the _____. **harp   carp**

8. An elf wears green and is _____. **fort   short**

9. Jordan got _____ on his feet at the beach. **bar   tar**

10. Use a flashlight to see in the _____. **dark   lark**

11. Brad started to _____ while he was sleeping. **snore   tore**

12. There is not much peanut butter left in the _____. **star   jar**

13. Put the _____ to the left of the plate. **fork   fort**

14. A peach that is not ripe may feel _____. **lard   hard**

15. Tie the box with _____ before you mail it. **lord   cord**

16. Jennifer made the baby's sweater with pink _____. **barn   yarn**

17. Maine is a state in the _____ part of the United States. **north   port**

18. We sent Mom a _____ on Mother's Day. **hard   card**

19. A tall bird with a long neck and beak is a _____. **stork   pork**

20. _____ are used for riding and carrying heavy loads. **Corns   Horses**

NAME _____

When the vowel **e, i,** or **u** is followed by the letter **r,** the vowel sound is neither long nor short. It is the vowel sound you hear in the words **fern, girl,** and **nurse.** Say each picture name. Circle the word that names the picture.

1.	2.	3.	4.
(curve) third swirl curl	bird burn churn church	curb fern burn surf	church nurse girl germ
5.	6.	7.	8.
germ curb clerk turn	herd hurt pure purse	shirt dirt clerk skirt	herd third first bird
9.	10.	11.	12.
turn bird burn churn	thirst curb curl perk	pure perk curl perch	thirty clerk third first
13.	14.	15.	16.
curb third herd church	fire skirt tire shirt	nerve germ nurse perch	curb turn herd twirl

Er, ir, and ur

Unit 6/Lesson 39 **83**

Read each sentence. Circle the word that completes the sentence. Then write the word on the line.

1. A small fish in a lake or stream is a _perch_____. (perch) church

2. Stroke a cat and it will _____. blur purr

3. "Mary Had a Little Lamb" is an old _____. nurse verse

4. In the fall, Woon will be in _____ grade. third bird

5. To make butter in a _____, stir the cream hard. burn churn

6. The class will have a test at the end of the _____. term germ

7. A tree that has cones is a _____. fir her

8. Do you tan or _____ in the sun? turn burn

9. At least forty cows were in the _____. herd curd

10. To reach King Street, _____ right at the corner. turn burn

11. Will the jay sit on its perch and _____? birch chirp

12. Anna has a gold ring and a _____ bracelet. winter silver

13. The shirt was so small that Chuck _____ the seams. burst first

14. Wash with soap to get rid of the _____ on your hands. germs terms

15. A silly kind of smile is a _____. irk smirk

16. Don't stop to play if you are in a _____. hurry curry

17. The painter used a stick to _____ the paint. fir stir

18. Popcorn and punch will be _____ at the party. served observed

19. The _____ asked how I was feeling. nurse curse

20. Sweep the porch to clean up the _____. dirt flirt

The letters **are, air,** or **ear** can stand for the same vowel sound, as in the words **care, hair,** and **pear.** Read each sentence. Circle the word that completes each sentence. Then write the word on the line.

1. We bought cheese and milk at the ___dairy___. (**dairy**) **hare**

2. Please _____ the cherries with Kim. **share lair**

3. Did you eat a peach or a _____? **mare pear**

4. Luis and Jay both have curly brown _____. **flare hair**

5. It is not safe to _____ at the sun. **stare pair**

6. A new baby needs a lot of _____. **fairy care**

7. The sharp tack made a _____ in my jeans. **tear stair**

8. Karen has to buy a new _____ of socks. **bare pair**

9. It is not _____ to cheat at a game. **fair wear**

10. The little cub felt safe with the big _____. **rare bear**

11. The van had a _____ tire in the back. **spare dairy**

12. Eric did not know which shirt to _____. **wear fair**

13. Mom is going to _____ the leak in the sink. **aware repair**

14. Is the cake round or _____? **air square**

15. Did the thunder in the play _____ you? **scare flair**

16. Carla likes to sit in the big tan _____. **dare chair**

17. The pup looked funny climbing the steep _____. **blare stairs**

18. I don't _____ go on that ride! **dare pair**

19. What is the bus _____ from Chicago to New York? **fare spare**

20. Chris likes taking long walks in the fresh _____. **air hair**

The letters **ear** can stand for three different vowel sounds, as in the words **earth, bear,** and **beard.** Read the words in the box. One word has two different sounds. It appears twice. Write each word below the picture that has the same vowel sound.

tear	bear	search	nearly
fear	learn	dear	hearse
heard	pearl	weary	early
pear	clear	yearn	rear
earl	year	wear	research
tear	earn	hear	smear

heard

Ear

Phonics in Action

Read the story.

Friends at the Fair

Cory and Blair go to the state fair at the park. Cory has art in a show there. Blair just wants to see the wares.

First, the friends go to the farm department. They watch horses prance and see hogs dig in the dirt. Blair giggles when she hears a hog snort. Cory nudges Blair so she can see a prize bird unfurl its wings.

Then the two friends spot a game. The barker yells for them to play. He thinks they cannot hit the mark. He tells Cory to get an arrow in a big jar. Cory has good aim. The first two arrows fall on the floor, but the third goes in the jar. Cory wins! She picks out a purse.

The friends get corn on the cob and wander through the park. They meet their friends Rory and Dirk. The four go to see Cory's art. They stay at the fair until dark.

Write the word on the line that completes each sentence about the story.

1. Cory and Blair see a _____ unfurl its wings.

2. The barker thinks Cory cannot hit the _____.

3. The friends get _____ on the cob.

Read the three words in each box. Circle all three words if they rhyme.

1. (yearn learn earn)	**2.** ear rear pearl	**3.** park mark dart	**4.** bird word herd
5. fear year dear	**6.** bear pear wear	**7.** spare care repair	**8.** hear tear shear
9. appear pear fair	**10.** burst first worst	**11.** smirk lurk work	**12.** curl unfurl curb
13. purr fir slur	**14.** barn yarn farm	purr blare blur	**16.** verse worse nurse

Read each sentence. Circle the letters that complete the unfinished word in the sentence. Then write the word on the line.

1. The car leaned to the left as it sped around the c_____ve. **ar ur ir**

2. The h_____e hopped into the bushes when it heard us. **ar ur ir**

3. Jill t_____e her coat on the playground. **er or ir**

4. Many h_____ds of buffalo once roamed the plains. **ear er ir**

5. Be careful not to b_____n the meat. **ir ur ar**

6. I wrote my name over and over until it was cl_____. **air ear are**

7. We will s_____ve fruit at the school picnic. **ar or er**

8. The balloon made a big bang when it b_____st. **ear ir ur**

9. It is Kim's t_____n to swing the jump rope. **ar ur ear**

10. The baby wanted to sm_____ food on her face. **ear are air**

11. C_____n can be eaten off the cob or on a plate. **ar ir or**

12. I think I can rep_____ this toy for my brother. **air oar ere**

13. Shall we all sit in a circle or a squ_____? **air are ere**

14. Jack wants to help the workers make the new b_____n. **ar ir ur**

15. Please add a squ_____t of lemon to my cold water. **ar ir ur**

16. We didn't want to be late so we got to the show _____ly. **air ere ear**

17. Jill plays the flute, and Harold plays the h_____p. **ir ar or**

18. In the summers, Luis w_____ks at jobs around the house. **or ir ear**

19. We saw an eagle s_____r into the sky out of sight. **ai oa ou**

20. Our yard is lined with flowers and f_____ns. **ir ar er**

Read each sentence. Choose a word from the box to complete each sentence. Then write the word on the line.

earth	bare	fairy	squirt	bears	beard
herd	arm	hurt	hair	torn	burn
rare	market	horn	bird	stern	wear

1. Kay broke a bone in her right _____.

2. Carlos put a new _____ on his bike.

3. Nancy used a hose to _____ her sister.

4. A _____ of horses roamed the plains.

5. If the flame is too high, the pot of beans will _____.

6. Will you _____ your tan skirt to the party?

7. Rosa likes to collect _____ stamps.

8. The _____ tale is about a king who loves gold.

9. Kurt was upset that his shirt was _____.

10. Frank is going to shave off his _____.

11. The _____ sat on eight eggs in the nest.

12. The astronauts took photographs of the _____ from space.

13. Jenny's dad went to buy meat at the _____.

14. Mr. Fong gave us a _____ talk on our table manners.

15. When Jordan fell off his bike, he was not _____.

16. I like to walk on the beach in my _____ feet.

17. When it gets cold, _____ sleep in caves.

18. The baby had very little _____ on her head.

TEST Vowels with **r**

The vowel letters **oo** can stand for the vowel sound you hear in the word **book** or the vowel sound you hear in the word **moon.** Say each picture name. Circle the word that names the picture.

1. good gloom	**2.** broom book	**3.** stool tool	**4.** nook cook
goose (groom)	brook rook	stood took	cool noon
5. foot root	**6.** stoop spoon	**7.** food hoot	**8.** zoo too
food fool	soot soon	hoof hood	zoom tooth
9. toot too	**10.** roof room	**11.** loom book	**12.** booth boom
boot book	tooth toot	look gloom	took tooth
13. roof hoof	**14.** hood noon	**15.** groove groom	**16.** wool good
hoot hood	moon mood	good goose	wood groove

Read each sentence. Circle the word that completes the sentence. Then write the word on the line.

1. What kind of food would a hungry ____moose____ eat? **moose   loose**

2. Wear a wool coat if you feel _____. **fool   cool**

3. Tina and her sister share a _____. **room   boom**

4. Will you bring in some more _____ for the fire? **hood   wood**

5. Hang up your coat on the _____. **hook   look**

6. When we went to the beach, we _____ our raft. **book   took**

7. A _____ of ice cream is the best treat. **droop   scoop**

8. Kevin is in the third grade at _____. **school   tool**

9. The toothpaste started to _____ from the tube. **ooze   choose**

10. During the earthquake, the whole city _____. **cook   shook**

11. Please sweep this room with a _____. **broom   groom**

12. Lee went to the art show to _____ at paintings. **hook   look**

13. We need a _____ of black thread to mend these pants. **spool   school**

14. The top of the table has a deep _____ in it. **soon   groove**

15. How long will it take to _____ the turkey? **cook   book**

16. The fireplace was filled with _____. **soot   root**

17. Jason eats lunch at _____. **soon   noon**

18. Eight chicks live in that _____. **coop   loop**

19. To vote, you must have _____ of where you live. **proof   goof**

20. This is where Grandma's home once _____. **good   stood**

Dipthongs **oo** (book) and **oo** (moon)

The letters **ow** can stand for the vowel sound you hear in the word **cow.** The letters **oy** stand for the vowel sound you hear in the word **boy.** Say each picture name. Circle the word that names the picture.

1.	**2.**	**3.**	**4.**
plow joy brown cow	towns toys boys brows	frown growl owl town	gown how now down
5.	**6.**	**7.**	**8.**
down shower flower frown	joy brown toy frown	clown how crown now	towel boy vowel toy
9.	**10.**	**11.**	**12.**
plow Roy brow toy	cow ploy how coy	joy brown brow boy	down clown crown gown
13.	**14.**	**15.**	**16.**
cow joy coy now	growl showers flowers fowl	vowels bow towels tow	owl fowl down town

Read each sentence. Circle the word that completes the sentence. Then
write the word on the line.

1. The spring storms <u>destroyed</u> many of the crops. (destroyed) employed

2. A bird that flies at night is the _____. **owl   now**

3. The queen climbed the steps to the top of the _____. **chow   tower**

4. At the circus we saw three funny _____. **brown   clowns**

5. A gnat buzzing around your head is very _____. **annoying   royal**

6. There are five banks in our _____. **town   brow**

7. Does Bill know _____ to drive a car? **fowl   how**

8. There are nine girls and _____ in the club. **enjoys   boys**

9. Dad and I plan to rinse the plates right _____. **now   bow**

10. The mean dog _____ as I walked by. **growled   allowed**

11. We were _____ when our team won the game. **envoy   joyful**

12. The mayor of our city has a lot of _____. **power   prows**

13. We drink milk that comes from _____. **howls   cows**

14. Did you _____ your trip to Canada? **enjoy   toys**

15. The field was full of pretty _____. **drowns   flowers**

16. The rock star waved to her fans in the _____. **crowd   plow**

17. My friend Rosa lets me play with her _____. **annoys   toys**

18. Tom has a new pair of _____ pants. **crown   brown**

19. After I jog, I take a _____ to get clean. **shower   frown**

20. My pup is very _____ to me. **loyal   enjoy**

Diphthongs **ow** and **oy**

The vowel letters **ou** can stand for the vowel sound you hear in the word **house**. The vowel letters **oi** stand for the vowel sound you hear in the word **soil**. Say each picture name. Circle the word that names the picture.

1.

count	(snout)
mount	shout

2.

coins	boil
coil	point

3.

couch	house
mouse	pouch

4.

sound	bound
pound	ground

5.

stout	spout
shout	scout

6.

oil	spoil
toil	coil

7.

bounce	couch
pouch	pound

8.

soil	noise
moist	toil

9.

house	broil
boil	blouse

10.

mount	moist
mouth	mouse

11.

count	moist
couch	mount

12.

boil	soil
toil	foil

13.

joint	pouch
point	couch

14.

scout	count
sound	found

15.

coil	cloud
loud	spoil

16.

coil	loud
coin	loin

Read each sentence. Circle the word that completes the sentence. Then write the word on the line.

1. The beef will __spoil__ if it is not kept in a cold place. (spoil) toil

2. There is a huge oak tree behind Tim's _____. **house   ouch**

3. Lucy wore a brown skirt and a tan _____. **found   blouse**

4. Many types of plants grow in that rich _____. **soil   join**

5. Do you like your eggs fried or _____? **noisy   boiled**

6. Rain will fall soon from those huge gray _____. **grounds   clouds**

7. You need _____ and eggs to bake a cake. **flour   sour**

8. We had a _____ of beans or rice with our meal. **choice   coin**

9. The _____ speaking on the phone was very deep. **moist   voice**

10. Juan _____ a short cut through the woods. **found   mound**

11. The little girl can _____ to one hundred. **count   ounce**

12. Put a _____ in the slot to make a phone call. **point   coin**

13. Ellen's dog weighs twenty _____. **pounds   scouts**

14. We could hear the _____ of a jet taking off. **crouch   sound**

15. Tom's bread stayed fresh because he wrapped it in _____. **foil   broil**

16. That steak knife has a very sharp _____. **avoid   point**

17. Ali draws well and wants to _____ an art club. **join   coil**

18. The seal carried the fish in its _____. **mouth   powder**

19. Vince sat on the _____ to watch TV. **noun   couch**

20. The grass was _____ after the brief shower. **moist   oil**

The letters **au, aw,** and **al** stand for the same vowel sound. It is the vowel sound you hear in the words **sauce, claw,** and **salt.** Say each picture name. Circle the word that names the picture.

1.

draw   paw
law   (jaw)

2.

straw   shawl
raw   saw

3.

crawl   shawl
chalk   walk

4.

claw   crawl
law   cause

5.

saw   malt
salt   halt

6.

shawl   saw
crawl   claw

7.

pawn   yawn
yawl   dawn

8.

vault   salt
fault   Paul

9.

dawn   raw
draw   paw

10.

auto   haul
hawk   lawn

11.

balk   hawk
walk   bald

12.

hawk   pause
Paul   haul

13.

saw   salt
sauce   shawl

14.

haul   paw
Paul   haunt

15.

cause   saw
fault   sauce

16.

haunt   halt
hawk   haul

Vowel combinations **au, aw,** and **al**

Read each sentence. Circle the word that completes the sentence. Then write the word on the line.

1. We saw _____stalks_____ of corn growing in the field. (stalks) talks

2. Ben _____ me how to play chess. **clause   taught**

3. The baby _____ on her hands and knees. **hawks   crawls**

4. The _____ in the sink is leaking. **faucet   pause**

5. Dad has a _____ spot on top of his head. **malt   bald**

6. The time when the sun rises is _____. **claw   dawn**

7. A lot of money is kept in a bank _____. **vault   cause**

8. Sarah's chore is to cut the _____ on Saturday. **lawn   shawl**

9. The pot roast is cooking in a thick brown _____. **maul   sauce**

10. Mr. Garcia wrote on the board with _____. **chalk   salt**

11. Can you _____ a map of your town? **yawn   draw**

12. There was a _____ in the TV show for some ads. **pause   haul**

13. Jack put too much _____ on his peas. **halt   salt**

14. The dog likes to _____ on meaty bones. **gnaw   raw**

15. It is no one's _____ that we lost the game. **haunt   fault**

16. The cat is licking the mud off its _____. **draw   paws**

17. The leader told the marchers to _____. **halt   chalk**

18. The people used a huge truck to _____ away the trash. **haul   clause**

19. Ms. Stern thinks the new rock song is _____. **hawk   awful**

20. Do you want an ice cream cone or a _____ milk? **malted   talk**

The letters **ew** can stand for the vowel sound you hear in the word **chew**.
The letters **ow** can stand for the vowel sound you hear in the word
snow. Say each picture name. Circle the word that names the picture.

1.	**2.**	**3.**	**4.**
threw stow (tow) flew	dew throw flow few	crow show screw new	grew low brew row
5.	**6.**	**7.**	**8.**
screw bowl own stew	new slow chew blow	grew stew show slow	mow sow blew drew
9.	**10.**	**11.**	**12.**
drew grew drown gown	flew low blew bow	row crew crow new	flew threw tow flow
13.	**14.**	**15.**	**16.**
new blow brew mow	show blew knew stew	snow crew screw sow	drew grow glow grew

Diphthongs **ew** and **ow**

Read each sentence. Circle the word that completes the sentence. Then write the word on the line.

1. There are just a _____few_____ slices of ham left. (few) dew

2. Is it easy to walk in a foot of _____? **glow snow**

3. Judy _____ a bone for her dog to catch. **threw new**

4. Would a moose eat with a spoon and a _____? **bowl slow**

5. Do you _____ how to train for a race? **flow know**

6. The sailboat went fast when the breeze _____. **knew blew**

7. Mr. Chang _____ a small, tan car. **owns grows**

8. A cold, clear stream _____ past the house. **flows sows**

9. The _____ of the jet helped us find our seats. **flew crew**

10. The cook made a delicious _____. **blew stew**

11. Would you _____ a new bulb into the lamp? **screw few**

12. Pam had the leading role in the _____. **mow show**

13. You have to _____ steak very well. **chew drew**

14. Eating the right food helps you to _____. **low grow**

15. When it got cool, the birds _____ south. **flew knew**

16. I will _____ the old rags in the trash. **low throw**

17. Ben didn't know what time it was, but Carol _____. **knew flew**

18. The shelf on the wall was too _____. **bowl low**

19. Are the tires on the van old or _____? **new dew**

20. A ride on a mule will be _____. **bow slow**

Diphthongs **ew** and **ow**

Phonics in Action

Read the story.

In the Woods

   Shelly and Roy live in a small house in the woods. Roy plows the soil. Shelly raises cows. On summer days, they kick off their boots and walk barefoot. Then they walk down to the brook to catch trout. Roy brings bait and a stool. Shelly brings a good book. They sit for hours on the banks or row a boat out into the brook. Roy sometimes talks quietly. Shelly is as quiet as a mouse.

   In the evenings, a goose that lives near the brook spoils the quiet. She and her goslings make lots of noise and scare the fish away. Then Roy and Shelly take some time off. They look for firewood. Then they roast corn and boil some roots. They wait for the moon to come up and for the geese to sleep.

   At night, the only sound is the call of a lone hawk or a loon. Sometimes, an owl hoots softly in the distance. Roy and Shelly enjoy the cool night air. Then they count the fish they have caught. They put on their boots and walk home, thinking that life is good.

Write the word on the line that completes each sentence about the story.

1. Roy plows the soil and Shelly raises _____.

2. The goose spoils the quiet by making _____.

3. Sometimes, an owl _____ softly.

Read the clues for the puzzle. Then write the word in the correct place in the puzzle.

Across

2. It means *going without shoes.*
3. Loud sounds are called this name.
5. You play with it. It rhymes with *boy.*
7. You have done this to a ball. It rhymes with *fought.*
9. When you don't ride, you do this.
11. It is a kind of bird. It rhymes with *soon.*
12. Farmers do this to loosen the soil.
15. It is a kind of fish. It rhymes with *snout.*

Down

1. When you were cold, you did this. It rhymes with *brook.*
2. You can sit in one at a diner. It rhymes with *tooth.*
4. A farmer does this to the soil.
5. You do this to tell something.
6. You do this with your hands or a shovel. It rhymes with *loop.*
8. You did this to get bigger. It rhymes with *dew.*
10. You can wear this on your foot. It rhymes with *hoot.*
13. You can fry foods in this. It rhymes with *boil.*
14. You do this to move a wagon.

Read each sentence. Circle the letters that complete the unfinished word in the sentence. Then write the letters on the line.

1. We are not all_____ed to go out after dark. **ow al ew**

2. When we are sleepy, we sometimes y_____n. **ew aw ow**

3. A dime is a kind of c_____n. **au oi ew**

4. Denise was t_____king on the phone to her aunt. **oy aw al**

5. When the sun rose, there was d_____ on the grass. **au ow ew**

6. Craig enj_____s doing the newest dances. **al oy ou**

7. Our dog eats its meals from a round, red b_____l. **ow oi aw**

8. Did the ball b_____nce past the player? **au ou oi**

9. This morning, Rita ate toast, eggs, and s_____sages. **ew oy au**

10. Don put his new shirt in the top dr_____er. **aw al ow**

11. The king's head hurt from his heavy cr_____n. **ow au oi**

12. Do you like your fish fried or br_____led? **oi ew au**

13. Ham is a very s_____ty meat. **oi ou al**

14. Our seats gave us a good vi_____ of the stage. **al ew ow**

15. Dianne will tie a big yellow b_____ on the box. **ow oi aw**

16. Terry will buy a game in the t_____ store. **al ow oy**

17. Limes have a very s_____r taste. **au ou oi**

18. A very high flame may c_____se the meat to burn. **au ow ou**

19. The huge jet made a lot of n_____se as it landed. **ew ou oi**

20. Judges and l_____yers both work in a court. **ou aw ow**

Read each sentence. Choose a word from the box to complete the sentence. Then write the word on the line.

mow	shook	mouth	chew	smooth	haunts
oil	coil	hoisted	fowl	bowling	halt
owl	good	fawn	woods	joy	loom

1. The rug was full of dust so Paul _____ it out.

2. The scout troop went for a hike in the _____.

3. We use teeth to bite and _____ our food.

4. Lisa will help Mark _____ the front lawn.

5. A chin, nose, and _____ are parts of a face.

6. Mom says tea with cream tastes _____.

7. They say an old sea captain _____ the house.

8. Jake made a heavy wool shawl on the _____.

9. The door will not squeak if you _____ it.

10. The game came to a _____ when it started to rain.

11. After Dad shaves his face, it feels _____.

12. The sailors will _____ the loose ropes.

13. Would a cow or an _____ hoot?

14. Ten wood pins and a heavy ball are used for _____.

15. Duck is _____, but beef is not.

16. Reading to her grandson is a real _____ for Grandma.

17. Spots on a _____ help it hide in the grass.

18. The huge crates were _____ onto the ship.

TEST Diphthongs and vowel combinations

A syllable is a word or part of a word. Each syllable has one vowel sound.

fox = 1 syllable   rabbit = 2 syllables

Say each picture name. Listen for the number of syllables, or word parts. Then on the line write the number of syllables in each word.

1.	2.	3.	4.	5.
2	___	___	___	___

6.	7.	8.	9.	10.
___	___	___	___	___

11.	12.	13.	14.	15.
___	___	___	___	___

16.	17.	18.	19.	20.
___	___	___	___	___

21.	22.	23.	24.	25.
___	___	___	___	___

One- and two-syllable words

A syllable is a word or part of a word. Each syllable has one vowel sound. There are as many syllables in a word as there are vowel sounds.

hen = 1 vowel letter   zebra = 2 vowel letters   grasshopper = 3 vowel letters

 1 vowel sound
1 syllable

 2 vowel sounds
2 syllables

 3 vowel sounds
3 syllables

In the first box, write the number of vowel letters you see in the word. Then say each picture name. In the second box, write the number of vowel sounds you hear in the word. In the third box, write the number of syllables in the word.

1.	2.	3.	4.
5.	6.	7.	8.
9.	10.	11.	12.
13.	14.	15.	16.

One-, two-, and three-syllable words

In a word that has two syllables, one syllable is usually said with more force, or stress. A stress mark (′) is placed at the end of the syllable that is said with more stress.

 bea′ ver   rac **coon′**

Say each picture name. Listen to the syllable that is said with more stress. Then put a stress mark at the end of the syllable that is stressed.

1. cam′ el	2. hel met	3. bal loon	4. pump kin	5. com pass
6. pen cil	7. cac tus	8. kitch en	9. cir cus	10. ig loo
11. ma chine	12. can dle	13. pil low	14. ba boon	15. tra peze
16. ca noe	17. trum pet	18. spi der	19. ho tel	20. brace let
21. har poon	22. col lie	23. car toon	24. drag on	25. ca nal

In a word that has three syllables, one syllable is usually said with more force, or stress. A stress mark (') is placed at the end of the syllable that is said with the most stress.

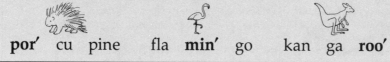

por′ cu pine   fla **min′** go   kan ga **roo′**

Say each picture name. Listen to the syllable that is said with the most stress. Then put a stress mark at the end of the syllable that is stressed most.

1. um brel la	**2.** pro pel ler	**3.** oc to pus	**4.** pa ja mas	**5.** go ril la
6. cel e ry	**7.** dom i no	**8.** croc o dile	**9.** pi an o	**10.** cer e al
11. com put er	**12.** fur ni ture	**13.** ex press way	**14.** grass hop per	**15.** whip poor will
16. par a keet	**17.** pro ject or	**18.** spa ghet ti	**19.** i gua na	**20.** di no saur
21. car na tion	**22.** mon o rail	**23.** to ma to	**24.** gro cer ies	**25.** po ta to

108   Unit 8/Lesson 51

Tip 1: Divide a compound word between the two words. Put the stress on the first syllable.

goldfish gold'/fish   windmill wind'/mill

Say each word listed below. On the line write the word, drawing a slash between the syllables. Put a stress mark at the end of the syllable that is stressed.

1. beehive _____bee'/hive_____

2. birthday _____

3. flashlight _____

4. doorknob _____

5. steamship _____

6. countdown _____

7. footstep _____

8. classroom _____

9. keyboard _____

10. fireplace _____

11. moonbeam _____

12. bookcase _____

13. snapshot _____

14. beefsteak _____

15. thumbtack _____

16. eyebrow _____

17. toothpaste _____

18. scarecrow _____

19. classroom _____

20. baseball _____

21. stringbean _____

22. spellbound _____

23. headache _____

24. backpack _____

25. snowplow _____

26. spacecraft _____

27. campfire _____

28. woodpile _____

29. drawbridge _____

30. outlaw _____

31. daytime _____

32. homework _____

Compound words   Unit 8/Lesson 52 **109**

Complete each sentence by choosing a compound word from the box.
Then write the word on the line.

greenhouse	tollbooth	homesick	lighthouse	workout	windmill
grapefruit	eyesight	outfield	earthquake	lifeguard	oatmeal
bedtime	seashore	notebook	password	pancake	snowfall

1. Jason likes to have a __grapefruit__ for breakfast every morning.

2. Last summer we went to the _____ for our family vacation.

3. An _____ causes fire and damages property.

4. Grandfather likes to spend time in the _____ with his plants.

5. I swim in the pool only when a _____ is on duty.

6. Roberto was _____ the first summer he went away to camp.

7. Cara ate the largest _____ on the plate.

8. Lynn wears glasses because she has poor _____.

9. Dad tells us stories at _____ to help us fall asleep.

10. The light from a _____ guides ships at night.

11. Fernando wrote his story in his _____.

12. For safety reasons, the guard changes the _____ every day.

13. Gail never misses a fly ball in the _____.

14. Victor likes cold milk with his _____ cookies.

15. Everyone on the team always showers after a long _____.

16. There is a _____ to collect money every twenty miles on the highway.

17. There was a 12-inch _____ last year on April 1.

18. A _____ can grind grain or pump water.

Compound words

Tip 2: Divide a word between the base word and its prefix. Put the stress on the base word.

unload   un/load'

Tip 3: Divide a word between the base word and its suffix. Put the stress on the base word.

catcher   catch'/er

Say each word listed below. Give the number of the tip that helps you to divide the word. Then write each word, drawing a slash between the syllables. Put a stress mark at the end of the base word to show that it is said with more stress.

1. unlock __2__ __un lock'__   2. painful ___ _____

3. dismount ___ _____   4. farmer ___ _____

5. careless ___ _____   6. dirty ___ _____

7. darkness ___ _____   8. thoughtful ___ _____

9. windy ___ _____   10. thickness ___ _____

11. softness ___ _____   12. helpless ___ _____

13. creamy ___ _____   14. thirsty ___ _____

15. retell ___ _____   16. neatly ___ _____

17. loudness ___ _____   18. wrongly ___ _____

19. sadness ___ _____   20. rewrap ___ _____

21. helpful ___ _____   22. curly ___ _____

23. quickly ___ _____   24. rewind ___ _____

25. lucky ___ _____   26. bumpy ___ _____

27. unfold ___ _____   28. dislike ___ _____

29. repack ___ _____   30. brightness ___ _____

31. fearless ___ _____   32. slowly ___ _____

Complete each sentence by choosing a word from the box. Then write the word on the line.

farmer	lucky	dislike	careless
painful	slowly	refill	dancer
gladness	repack	brightness	loudness
hopeful	finally	unlock	useless

1. Hitting your elbow against a doorknob can be very ___painful___ .

2. Vinny had to _____ his suitcase so everything would fit.

3. Ernie and Hal hope today is their _____ day.

4. Here is the key to _____ the door.

5. Rita and Jill like grapefruits but _____ melons.

6. The _____ of the music gave Kate a headache.

7. Sunglasses protect my eyes from the _____ of the sun.

8. Louise rushed through the test and made _____ mistakes.

9. Georgia _____ made it to the top of the mountain.

10. A _____ plants crops in spring and harvests them in the fall.

11. Joey is studying to become a ballet _____ .

12. Will you please _____ my glass with water?

13. Ride your bike _____ over the bumpy road.

14. There was much _____ when our team won first prize.

15. A knife with a dull blade is _____ .

16. Carmen was _____ about winning until the last jump.

Syllables, prefixes, and suffixes

Tip 4: When the first vowel sound is followed by two consonants, divide the word between the two consonants. Put the stress on the first syllable. Then say the first vowel with a short sound unless it is followed by **r**.

kĭt´/ten	prĕt´/zel	splĭn´/ter	har´/vest	pĭc´/ture
↑↑↑ ↑↑↑	↑ ↑↑ ↑↑↑	↑ ↑↑ ↑↑↑	↑↑↑ ↑↑↑	↑↑↑ ↑↑↑↑
c v c c v c	c v c c v c	c v c c v c	c v c c v c	c v c c v c e

Read each two-syllable word listed below. On the line write the word, drawing a slash between the syllables. In the first syllable, mark the vowel letter with a ˘ if it is said with a short sound or underline the vowel with **r**. Then put a stress mark at the end of the syllable that is said with more stress.

1. shelter   shĕl´/ter
2. splatter   _____
3. panther   _____
4. carrot   _____
5. pilgrim   _____
6. practice   _____
7. carbon   _____
8. terror   _____
9. pennant   _____
10. batter   _____
11. scrimmage   _____
12. suffer   _____
13. dictate   _____
14. harbor   _____
15. garden   _____
16. message   _____
17. ransom   _____
18. borrow   _____
19. gallon   _____
20. gallop   _____
21. splendid   _____
22. hornet   _____
23. narrow   _____
24. garbage   _____
25. cabbage   _____
26. suffix   _____
27. mixture   _____
28. signal   _____

Read each sentence. Circle the word that completes the sentence. Then write the word on the line.

1. Angie needs a ___carrot___ and some peppers for her salad. **mammal** (**carrot**)

2. The road by the town bridge is _____ and curvy. **narrow** **garnet**

3. The king and queen live in a _____ old palace. **galley** **splendid**

4. The fierce black _____ could not be seen at night. **couch** **panther**

5. Joel has his school _____ on a wall in his bedroom. **service** **pennant**

6. Liz, Lou, and Lia huddled under the umbrella for _____. **shelter** **signal**

7. The survivors of the flood were filled with _____. **terror** **border**

8. There is baseball _____ this Saturday morning at 9 o'clock. **practice** **scrimmage**

9. Mom left a _____ for us on the front door. **mixture** **message**

10. May I _____ your pearl necklace for the party on Sunday? **borrow** **gallop**

11. A sting from a _____ can be very painful. **hornet** **pretzel**

12. Pat will take the _____ outside after dinner. **garden** **garbage**

13. You need to polish silver often or it will _____. **splatter** **tarnish**

14. My dad goes to the _____ for a haircut and shave. **pilgrim** **barber**

15. Arlene makes the best _____ bread I have ever eaten. **carbon** **garlic**

16. Rush hour _____ caused a long delay on the highway. **traffic** **ransom**

17. Manuel needs a large _____ to fry the bacon and eggs. **skillet** **scrimmage**

18. The rocking chair belongs in that _____ of the room. **kitten** **corner**

Read the tips for dividing words into syllables. For each word listed below, give the number of the tip that helps you to divide the word. Then write the word, drawing a slash between the syllables.

> **Tip 1:** Divide a compound word between the two words. (dog/house)
> **Tip 2:** Divide a word between the base word and its prefix. (re/place)
> **Tip 3:** Divide a word between the base word and its suffix. (care/less)
> **Tip 4:** When the first vowel sound is followed by two consonants, divide the word between the two consonants. Say the first vowel with a short sound unless it is followed by **r**. (man/ner, har/vest)

1. steamship _1_ steam/ship

2. yellow __ _____

3. dismount __ _____

4. stringbean __ _____

5. curly __ _____

6. garden __ _____

7. snapshot __ _____

8. unwind __ _____

9. narrow __ _____

10. fearless __ _____

11. refill __ _____

12. homework __ _____

13. toothpaste __ _____

14. rewrap __ _____

15. brightness __ _____

16. neatly __ _____

17. unfold __ _____

18. fireplace __ _____

19. catcher __ _____

20. practice __ _____

21. mammal __ _____

22. dislike __ _____

23. terrace __ _____

24. careful __ _____

25. dirty __ _____

26. border __ _____

27. eyesight __ _____

28. refuel __ _____

Read each sentence. Circle the word that completes the sentence. Then write the word on the line.

1. Georgia has her mother's _____curly_____ hair. bumpy (curly)

2. Someday I want to travel around the world on a _____. steamship moonbeam

3. Mel forgot his camera and could not take any _____. thumbtacks snapshots

4. The _____ and curvy street is very dangerous. hornet narrow

5. Please _____ the bucket so we can water the plants. refill rewrap

6. Don't let the paint _____ the floor. splatter splinter

7. Is there any _____ left in the tube? headache toothpaste

8. The _____ of the sun almost blinded me. cloudless brightness

9. _____ the tablecloth to see if it needs to be ironed. Unfold Retie

10. The kitchen area on a ship is called a _____. galley gallon

11. My pocket caught on the _____ and ripped. doorknob doorway

12. Do you like or _____ loud music? dislike dismounts

13. Not one _____ in my garden is ripe yet. stringbean goldfish

14. _____ the rope so we can see how much is left. Unlock Unwind

15. Please _____ the window so we can feel a breeze. open apron

16. Rosa must finish her _____ before she can play. homework classroom

17. The soldier in uniform was _____ dressed. neatly politely

18. Let's sit out on the _____ where it is cooler. terrace harbor

REVIEW Syllables, compound words, prefixes, suffixes, and syllable patterns

Tip 5: When the first vowel sound is followed by one consonant or consonant sound, read the word. If the first vowel has a long sound, divide the word before the consonant. Put the stress on the first syllable.

$$\overline{r}\overline{o}\,'/bot \qquad p\overline{i}'/rate$$
$$\underset{cv}{\uparrow\uparrow}\ \underset{cvc}{\uparrow\uparrow\uparrow} \qquad \underset{cv}{\uparrow\uparrow}\ \underset{cvce}{\uparrow\uparrow\uparrow\uparrow}$$

Tip 6: When a vowel is sounded alone in a word, it forms a syllable in itself. Put the stress on the first syllable. Then say the vowel with a long sound.

$$\overline{a}'\,/pron$$
$$\underset{cvc}{\uparrow}$$

Read each two-syllable word listed below. On the line write the word, drawing a slash between the syllables. In the first syllable, mark the vowel letter with a ˉ to show that it is said with a long sound. Then put a stress mark at the end of the syllable that is said with more stress.

1. crater _crā'/ter_
2. nature _____
3. secret _____
4. vapor _____
5. radar _____
6. spiral _____
7. decent _____
8. woven _____
9. climate _____
10. rival _____
11. gopher _____
12. minor _____
13. lunar _____
14. laser _____
15. broken _____
16. donate _____
17. visor _____
18. cubic _____
19. legal _____
20. driver _____
21. vacant _____
22. vacate _____
23. cedar _____
24. crisis _____

Read each sentence. Circle the word that completes the sentence. Then write the word on the line.

1. An __acorn__ just fell from the oak tree by the garage. (acorn) apron

2. I wish I had a _____ to do my errands! **diver robot**

3. The story is about a _____ who sails the seven seas. **pirate crater**

4. Carlos wants to _____ his prize to the school. **notice donate**

5. The _____ in the South is very warm and humid. **crater climate**

6. The coffee was _____ with the rim of the cup. **evil even**

7. Can a _____ dig an underground tunnel? **radar gopher**

8. Jonathan wants to be an airline _____. **secret pilot**

9. A _____ or unsharpened pencil is useless. **human broken**

10. That _____ stairway leads to the choir loft. **spiral robot**

11. Please help me _____ the locked chest. **odor open**

12. Dad always wears a _____ when it's sunny. **visor vapor**

13. Will you help me _____ New Orleans on this map? **notice locate**

14. The apple trees on the front lawn are of _____ height. **equal secret**

15. An egg has an _____ rather than a round shape. **oval rival**

16. _____ heating keeps our house warm and dry in winter. **Solar Nature**

17. There is a _____ on the board about play practice. **notice crisis**

18. We must _____ our hotel room by noon today. **vacate donate**

Syllable patterns cv/cvc and cv/cvce

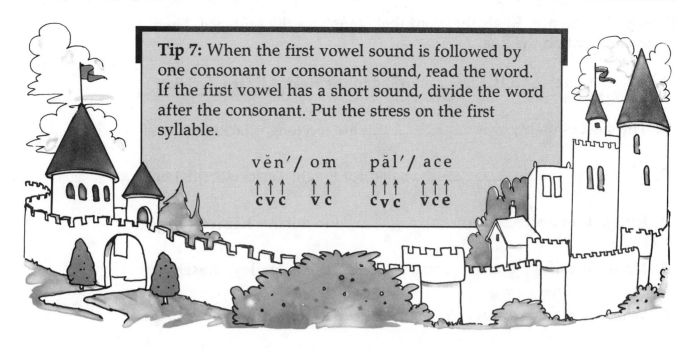

Tip 7: When the first vowel sound is followed by one consonant or consonant sound, read the word. If the first vowel has a short sound, divide the word after the consonant. Put the stress on the first syllable.

věn′/ om   păl′/ ace
↑↑↑ ↑↑   ↑↑↑ ↑↑↑
c v c v c   c v c v c e

Read each two-syllable word listed below. On the line write the word, drawing a slash between the syllables. In the first syllable, mark the vowel letter with a ˘ to show that it is said with a short sound. Then put a stress mark at the end of the syllable that is said with more stress.

1. radish   răd′/ish

2. clinic _____

3. jacket _____

4. shrivel _____

5. chicken _____

6. spirit _____

7. figure _____

8. lizard _____

9. cricket _____

10. nickel _____

11. hazard _____

12. topic _____

13. rebel _____

14. rather _____

15. wither _____

16. mimic _____

17. desert _____

18. legend _____

19. manage _____

20. damage _____

21. relish _____

22. planet _____

23. ticket _____

24. spinach _____

25. camper _____

26. savage _____

27. devil _____

28. whether _____

Read each sentence. Circle the word that completes the sentence. Then write the word on the line.

1. Listen to that __cricket__ chirping in the field.   lizard   (cricket)

2. The sleeves on my new _____ are too long.   **jacket**   **planet**

3. I would like cold _____ salad for lunch.   **cricket**   **chicken**

4. Icy roads and streets are a _____ in winter.   **hazard**   **haggard**

5. Many beautiful plants grow in a _____.   **galley**   **desert**

6. When I am older, I want to _____ a store.   **figure**   **manage**

7. Frank likes to put _____ on his hot dog.   **relish**   **topic**

8. Jay must buy a _____ before going into the movie.   **spirit**   **ticket**

9. Our _____ is equipped for long trips.   **camper**   **lizard**

10. Please add a sliced _____ to my green salad.   **jacket**   **radish**

11. Without water, flowers will _____ up and die.   **damage**   **shrivel**

12. There are five pennies in a _____.   **legend**   **nickel**

13. Josie would _____ read a book than watch television.   **manage**   **rather**

14. It makes no difference _____ we win or lose.   **relish**   **whether**

15. We will _____ our toys and put them away.   **whether**   **gather**

16. John was so cold he started to _____.   **palace**   **shiver**

17. An early frost can _____ a farmer's crop.   **gather**   **damage**

18. The _____ pirate filled the captives with terror.   **palace**   **savage**

Syllable patterns cvc/vc, cvc/vce

Tip 8: When a word ends in a consonant plus **le**, divide the word before the consonant. Put the stress on the first syllable.

mā′/ple   crŭm′/ble   tur̆′/tle

If the letters **ck** come before the **le**, divide the word before the **le**.

crăck′/le   tĭck′/le

Read each two-syllable word listed below. On the line write the word, drawing a slash between the syllables. In the first syllable, mark the vowel letter with a ˘ if it is said with a short sound. Mark it with ¯ if it is said with a long sound. Circle the syllable if it contains a vowel with **r**. Then put a stress mark at the end of the syllable that is said with more stress. Remember that **c + le** is a syllable.

1. puzzle _____pŭz′/zle_____

2. candle _____

3. little _____

4. bundle _____

5. riddle _____

6. freckle _____

7. table _____

8. ladle _____

9. rattle _____

10. cable _____

11. thimble _____

12. heckle _____

13. drizzle _____

14. cradle _____

15. stumble _____

16. kernel _____

17. kettle _____

18. single _____

19. knuckle _____

20. simple _____

21. uncle _____

22. buckle _____

23. fiddle _____

24. speckle _____

25. apple _____

26. tumble _____

27. ruffle _____

28. giggle _____

29. circle _____

30. nimble _____

31. throttle _____

32. sickle _____

33. rubble _____

34. middle _____

Read each sentence. Circle the word that completes the sentence. Then write the word on the line.

1. The sound of the ___bugle___ awakens us each day at camp. **tickle** (**bugle**)

2. Kim is so clumsy that she always _____ the ball. **grumbles   fumbles**

3. Look at the _____ floating in the air! **speckle   bubble**

4. The weather forecast is for a slight _____. **fizzle   drizzle**

5. My pony is very happy in the new _____. **jungle   stable**

6. It is very simple to _____ a fire. **bundle   kindle**

7. Kara wears a fancy belt with a silver _____. **candle   buckle**

8. The _____ near the lake is huge and empty. **turtle   castle**

9. Use the _____ to take the gravy out of the pot. **cattle   ladle**

10. A huge _____ supports the town bridge. **drizzle   cable**

11. A _____ is a story about animals who act like people. **fable   rattle**

12. The _____ soared up into the bright blue sky. **kettle   eagle**

13. Fasten your papers together with a _____. **bundle   staple**

14. This mouthwash makes your mouth _____. **puddle   tingle**

15. A _____ cable connected the car to the tow truck. **single   bubble**

16. The _____ on that pan gets very hot. **handle   bottle**

17. _____ are usually raised on large ranches. **Middle   Cattle**

18. Tina wants to buy a silver _____ for her mother. **thimble   purple**

Read the tips for dividing words into syllables. For each word listed below, give the number of the tip that helps you to divide the word. Then write the word, drawing a slash between the syllables.

> **Tip 4:** When the first vowel sound is followed by two consonants, divide the word between the two consonants. Say the first vowel with a short sound unless it is followed by **r**. (man/ner, har/vest)
>
> **Tip 5:** When the first vowel sound is followed by one consonant or consonant sound, read the word. If the first vowel has a long sound, divide the word before the consonant. (ro/bot, pi/rate)
>
> **Tip 6:** When a vowel is sounded alone in a word, it forms a syllable in itself. Say the vowel with a long sound. (a'pron)
>
> **Tip 7:** When the first vowel sound is followed by one consonant or consonant sound, read the word. If the first vowel has a short sound, divide the word after the consonant. (ven/om, pal/ace)
>
> **Tip 8:** When a word ends in a consonant plus **le**, divide the word before the consonant. (ma/ple, crum/ble) If **ck** comes before **le**, divide the word before **le**. (pick/le)

1. candle _7_ __can/dle__
2. trickle ___ _____
3. chicken ___ _____
4. cable ___ _____
5. freckle ___ _____
6. damage ___ _____
7. wither ___ _____
8. cradle ___ _____
9. ladle ___ _____
10. iris ___ _____
11. pirate ___ _____
12. robot ___ _____
13. decent ___ _____
14. struggle ___ _____
15. saddle ___ _____
16. planet ___ _____
17. tackle ___ _____
18. bugle ___ _____
19. mammal ___ _____
20. gallon ___ _____
21. noble ___ _____
22. better ___ _____
23. border ___ _____
24. music ___ _____
25. carrot ___ _____
26. paper ___ _____
27. handle ___ _____
28. ankle ___ _____

Read each sentence. Circle the word that completes the sentence. Then write the word on the line.

1. The ___handle___ on the coffeepot is broken. (handle) cradle

2. The player tried not to _____ the ball. **tumble   fumble**

3. What _____ in the galaxy would you like to visit? **camper   planet**

4. The lace _____ on the curtains is very delicate. **ruffle   saddle**

5. May I borrow a sheet of _____? **paper   pilot**

6. The baby is sound asleep in the _____. **apple   cradle**

7. Ice and cold can _____ spring flowers. **damage   cabbage**

8. Gerri's _____ wakes up the whole camp. **single   bugle**

9. There is a breeze coming through the _____ door. **open   apron**

10. The song says, "_____ while you work." **Whistle   Thistle**

11. An _____ is a flower, not a gemstone. **iris   evil**

12. Unlike me, my brother does not have a single _____. **heckle   freckle**

13. In a dry climate, ivy will _____ and die. **wither   rather**

14. _____ stories always involve action and adventure. **Nature   Pirate**

15. Please turn up the radio so we can hear the _____. **music   paper**

16. It is not very difficult to _____ a fire. **tackle   kindle**

17. _____ signals help the coast guard to find the ship. **Radar   Spiral**

18. Look at that enormous _____ on the rock! **bubble   beetle**

REVIEW Syllable patterns

The schwa sound is a vowel sound heard in many words of two or more syllables. It is neither a long nor a short vowel sound. The schwa sound is heard in an unstressed syllable. Each vowel letter — **a, e, i, o, u** — can stand for this soft sound. The symbol for the schwa sound is ə.

sal**a**d   kitch**e**n   g**i**raffe   drag**o**n   wal**ru**s

Say each picture name. Listen to the sound of the underlined letter in each word. Then circle the symbol of the sound for the underlined letter.

1.	2.	3.	4.	5.
zebr**a**	barr**e**l	m**e**ter	ch**i**mney	p**e**ncil

6.	7.	8.	9.	10.
ti**ge**r	d**i**vide	t**a**ble	pill**o**w	lem**o**n

11.	12.	13.	14.	15.
escalator	c**a**nnon	pil**o**t	octop**u**s	alb**u**m

16.	17.	18.	19.	20.
b**o**nnet	m**u**sic	cact**u**s	can**o**e	d**i**nosaur

21.	22.	23.	24.	25.
skel**e**ton	alph**a**bet	ribb**o**n	carr**o**t	apr**o**n

Read each sentence. Circle the letter in the underlined word that
stands for the schwa.

1. Lynn always wears an apr**o**n when she washes the supper dishes.

2. There are lots of trees and shrubs <u>around</u> our house and in our yard.

3. If you buy a new bat now, you will get a <u>bonus</u>.

4. I can spell all the words in the left <u>column</u>.

5. The <u>chorus</u> will sing all the songs in the play.

6. We need a carrot, a pepper, some mushrooms, and lettuce for the <u>salad</u>.

7. A three-ring <u>circus</u> comes to our town every spring and fall.

8. The old bridge will <u>collapse</u> with all that heavy truck traffic.

9. Kate likes to eat steaks that are rare and <u>tender</u>.

10. Carl needs help to <u>dial</u> a long-distance phone number.

11. We gave Grandfather a <u>silver</u> watch for his birthday.

12. That <u>giraffe</u> must be the tallest animal in the local zoo.

13. A grilled <u>salmon</u> steak is tasty and delicious.

14. Thirty <u>minus</u> five is twenty-five.

15. Connie has not <u>spoken</u> to Arnold and Vinny in three weeks.

16. Larry forgot to leave a <u>margin</u> when he typed the letter to the editor.

17. The robot stopped working when its computer <u>system</u> failed.

18. To me, the zebra is one of the strangest <u>animals</u> in the zoo.

A syllable is a word or part of a word. Each syllable has one vowel sound.

gorilla = 3 syllables   caterpillar = 4 syllables

Say each picture name. Listen for the number of syllables, or word parts. Then write the number of syllables in each word on the line.

1. ___4___	2. _____	3. _____	4. _____	5. _____
6. _____	7. _____	8. _____	9. _____	10. _____
11. _____	12. _____	13. _____	14. _____	15. _____
16. _____	17. _____	18. _____	19. _____	20. _____
21. _____	22. _____	23. _____	24. _____	25. _____

In a word that has more than two syllables, one syllable is usually said with the most force, or stress. A stress mark ´ is placed at the end of the syllable that is said with the most stress.

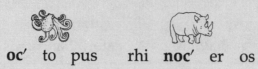

oc′ to pus   rhi **noc′** er os

Say each picture name. Listen to the syllable that is said with the most stress. Then put a stress mark at the end of the syllable that is stressed most.

1. dan de li on	**2.** zin ni a	**3.** wheel bar row	**4.** veg e ta bles	**5.** tel e vis ion
6. vol ca no	**7.** vi o lin	**8.** vi o lets	**9.** ther mom e ter	**10.** spa ghet ti
11. um brel la	**12.** tri an gle	**13.** ge ra ni um	**14.** val en tine	**15.** pho tog ra pher
16. tram po line	**17.** straw ber ry	**18.** pro pel ler	**19.** chim pan zee	**20.** grass hop per
21. to ma to	**22.** kan ga roo	**23.** mar i o nette	**24.** hel i cop ter	**25.** wa ter mel on

Stressed syllables

Read the tips for dividing words into syllables. For each word listed below, give the number of the tip that helps you to divide the word. Then write the word, drawing a slash between the syllables.

Tip 1: Divide a compound word between the two words. (dog/house)

Tip 2: Divide a word between the base word and its prefix. (re/place)

Tip 3: Divide a word between the base word and its suffix. (care/less)

Tip 4: When the first vowel sound is followed by two consonants, divide the word between the two consonants. Say the first vowel with a short sound unless it is followed by **r.** (man/ner, har/vest)

Tip 5: When the first vowel sound is followed by one consonant or consonant sound, read the word. If the first vowel has a long sound, divide the word before the consonant. (ro/bot, pi/rate)

Tip 6: When a vowel is sounded alone in a word, it forms a syllable in itself. Say the vowel with a long sound. (a/pron)

Tip 7: When the first vowel sound is followed by one consonant or consonant sound, read the word. If the first vowel has a short sound, divide the word after the consonant. (ven/om, pal/ace)

Tip 8: When a word ends in a consonant plus **le,** divide the word before the consonant. (ma/ple, crum/ble) If **ck** comes before **le,** divide the word before **le.** (pick/le)

1. pretzel   _4_ pret/zel

2. gopher   __ _____

3. pancake   __ _____

4. lizard   __ _____

5. homeless   __ _____

6. platter   __ _____

7. double   __ _____

8. maple   __ _____

9. sunset   __ _____

10. dismount   __ _____

11. unload   __ _____

12. farmer   __ _____

13. thoughtful   __ _____

14. airplane   __ _____

15. manage   __ _____

16. splinter   __ _____

17. crackle   __ _____

18. repack   __ _____

19. robot   __ _____

20. tickle   __ _____

21. nickel   __ _____

22. football   __ _____

Complete each sentence by choosing a word from the box. Then write
the word on the line.

cactus	bacon	lunar	walrus
lucky	freckle	divide	sandwich
oven	shelter	birthday	nickel
barrel	ribbon	unlock	message

1. Walter likes to eat _____bacon_____ and eggs for breakfast.

2. A _____ has no leaves and grows best in hot, dry places.

3. Brenda baked the chicken in the _____ for one hour.

4. Manuel needs to _____ the garage so he can put his bike away.

5. Will you _____ the pie into eight pieces?

6. Maureen was very _____ to win a computer.

7. Steve wants a fish salad _____ for lunch.

8. Kara Marie's _____ is March 13.

9. The book tells about the astronauts and their _____ landing.

10. Let's wrap the present with a bright and colorful _____.

11. Marie took the lost kitten to the animal _____.

12. There is water in the _____ near the porch.

13. The only change Rosa has left is a _____ and two quarters.

14. Pat has a cute _____ on the tip of her nose.

15. Do you think a seal and a _____ look alike?

16. Mom left a _____ for Dad near the telephone.

Say each word listed below. On the line write the word, drawing a
slash between the syllables.

1. puddle _____ 2. fable _____

3. daytime _____ 4. sadness _____

5. dislike _____ 6. harbor _____

7. radar _____ 8. odor _____

9. cricket _____ 10. riddle _____

11. apple _____ 12. buckle _____

13. classroom _____ 14. painful _____

15. agent _____ 16. rewrap _____

17. picture _____ 18. uncle _____

19. thimble _____ 20. secret _____

Say each word listed below. On the line write the word, drawing a
slash between the syllables. Put a stress mark at the end of the syllable
or base word that is said with more stress.

1. drizzle _____ 2. gobble _____

3. camel _____ 4. helmet _____

5. circus _____ 6. lemon _____

7. barrel _____ 8. igloo _____

9. creamy _____ 10. pillar _____

11. unlock _____ 12. replace _____

13. campfire _____ 14. toothpaste _____

15. album _____ 16. pencil _____

17. compass _____ 18. candle _____

19. robin _____ 20. turtle _____

21. spider _____ 22. radish _____

23. dislike _____ 24. skillet _____

Read the story below. The circle all the names of animals. Say each name and decide if it has three or four syllables. Then write the words on the lines below the story. Remember to use each word only once.

At the zoo, Henrietta and Jerome usually go to the Ape House first where the gorillas, the chimpanzees, and the orangutan show off just for them. Next, they run to the "African Animals" exhibit. Jerome says he likes the way the rhinoceros, the elephants, and the antelope roam about as if they were back in Africa.

At the Reptile and Amphibian House, everything from salamanders to crocodiles gives Henrietta and Jerome the shivers. An alligator shows its teeth to them. The iguana reminds Jerome of a living dinosaur.

When they feel brave enough, Henrietta and Jerome enter the Insect Room to see how those little caterpillars turn into beautiful butterflies. Still, the tarantula and the scorpion scare them both.

"I like the small animals better, especially the opossum, the armadillo, and the porcupine," says Henrietta. "They seem shy and more interested in being friends."

Henrietta saved her Australian favorites, the kangaroo, the koala, and the platypus, for the end of her visit. Jerome would like a koala for a pet, but since that can't be, he and Henrietta plan to visit the zoo again next week.

3-syllable words

_____   _____   _____   _____

_____   _____   _____   _____

_____   _____   _____   _____

4-syllable words

_____   _____   _____   _____

_____   _____   _____   _____

When a word ends in a single consonant and the vowel sound is short, double the consonant before adding **ed, ing, er,** or **est.** There is no spelling change when adding **s.**

flap flap**s** flap**ped** flap**ping**

sad sad**der** sad**dest**

Read each word listed below. Add the endings **s, ed,** and **ing** to each word. Then write the words on the lines.

	s	ed	ing
1. wrap	wraps	wrapped	wrapping
2. fit			
3. skim			
4. clip			
5. play			
6. jog			
7. slip			
8. plan			
9. wag			

Read each word listed bwlow. Add the endings **er** and **est** to each word. Then write the words on the lines.

	er	est		er	est
1. hot	hotter	hottest	**2.** mad		
3. slim			**4.** red		
5. flat			**6.** dull		
7. big			**8.** thin		
9. cool			**10.** dim		

> When a word ends in silent **e**, drop the **e** before adding **ed, ing, er,** or **est.** There is no spelling change when adding **s.**
>
> divide divid**es** divid**ed** divid**ing**
>
> large larg**er** larg**est**

Read each word listed below. Add the endings **s, ed,** and **ing** to each word. Then write the words on the lines.

	s	ed	ing
1. trace	traces	traced	tracing
2. hope			
3. jump			
4. slice			
5. please			
6. question			
7. explore			
8. examine			
9. damage			

Read each word listed below. Add the endings **er** and **est** to each word. Then write the words on the lines.

	er	est		er	est
1. late	later	latest	**2.** white		
3. tame			**4.** ripe		
5. brave			**6.** sure		
7. safe			**8.** blue		
9. long			**10.** true		
11. tall			**12.** close		

Inflectional endings **s, ed, ing, er,** and **est**

> When a word ends in **y** with a consonant before it, change the **y** to **i** before adding **es**, **ed**, **er**, or **est**. There is no spelling change when adding **ing**.
>
> berry berr**ies**
>
> cry cr**ies** cr**ied** cry**ing**
>
> heavy heav**ier** heav**iest**

Read each word listed below. Add the ending **s** or **es** to each word to make it plural. The write the word on the line.

1. pony _ponies_ **2.** lily _____ **3.** monkey _____

4. puppy _____ **5.** party _____ **6.** hobby _____

7. key _____ **8.** copy _____ **9.** country _____

Read each word listed below. Add the endings **s** or **es**, **ed**, and **ing** to each word. Then write the words on the lines.

	s or es	ed	ing
1. reply	replies	replied	replying
2. bury			
3. empty			
4. delay			
5. deny			

Read each word listed below. Add the endings **er** and **est** to each word. Then write the words on the lines.

	er	est		er	est
1. fuzzy	fuzzier	fuzziest	**2.** chilly		
3. merry			**4.** gray		
5. breezy			**6.** noisy		
7. ugly			**8.** sticky		

When a word ends in **x, s, ss, sh,** or **ch,** add **es** to make the word plural, or mean more than one.

For some words ending in **f** or **fe,** change the **f** or **fe** to **v** before adding **es** to make the word plural.

ostrich   ostrich**es**   calf   calv**es**

Read each word listed below. Add the ending **s** or **es** to each word to make it plural. Then write the word on the line.

1. branch   _branches_

2. fox   _____

3. ax   _____

4. scratch   _____

5. torch   _____

6. brush   _____

7. box   _____

8. loss   _____

9. river   _____

10. church   _____

11. gas   _____

12. kiss   _____

13. latch   _____

14. planet   _____

15. cross   _____

16. annex   _____

17. wish   _____

18. bus   _____

Read each word listed below. Add the ending **s** or **es** to each word to make it plural. Then write the word on the line.

1. half   _halves_

2. elf   _____

3. leaf   _____

4. wife   _____

5. knife   _____

6. wolf   _____

7. shelf   _____

8. scarf   _____

9. owl   _____

10. life   _____

11. loaf   _____

12. balloon   _____

13. thief   _____

14. self   _____

15. farm   _____

16. wharf   _____

To show that an object belongs to one person or thing, add **'s** to the end of the word.

Bill**'s** bicycle   the trumpet**'s** sound

To show that an object belongs to more than one person or thing, add **'** to the end of the word.

the doctors**'** fees   the chairs**'** backs

Look at each picture. Then read the sentence. Circle the word that completes the sentence. Then write the word on the line.

1. Your ___dog's___ water bowl needs to be filled.	(dog's) dogs'
2. A _____ toys were scattered all over the floor.	baby's babies'
3. Those _____ strokes were long and powerful.	swimmer's swimmers'
4. All of the _____ points were broken.	pencil's pencils'
5. This _____ claws need to be trimmed.	cat's cats'
6. Those _____ fragrances filled the air.	flower's flowers'
7. The pond is three _____ homes for the summer.	duck's ducks'
8. There is one _____ chair on the beach.	lifeguard's lifeguards'

Singular and plural possessive forms

> The plural of some words is formed by changing one or more letters in the word.
>
> mouse mice   goose geese   ox oxen
>
> Some words have the same spelling in their singular and plural forms.
>
> moose sheep deer salmon trout flounder

Look at each picture. Read the words under the picture. Then circle the word that names each picture.

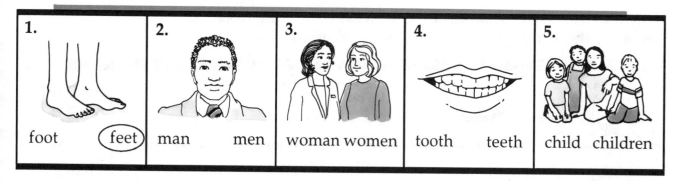

1. foot (feet) 2. man men 3. woman women 4. tooth teeth 5. child children

Look at each picture. Then on the line write the word that names each picture.

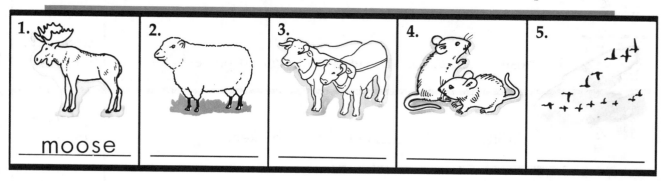

1. moose 2. _____ 3. _____ 4. _____ 5. _____

Complete each sentence by choosing a word from above. Then write the word on the line.

1. There are three ___children___ in our family.

2. Roberto's new ice skates fit his _____ perfectly.

3. _____ helped pull pioneer wagons across the country.

4. Many _____ and _____ worked to build that new building.

5. The wool from _____ is used to make clothes.

6. On our visit to the poultry farm, we saw chickens, ducks, and _____.

7. Maria has three large cavities in her _____.

8. _____ have broader antlers than deer.

Irregular plural forms

Read each sentence. Add the ending **s, ed, ing, er,** or **est** to each word to complete the sentence. Then write the word on the line. You may need to make spelling changes.

1. Sonia ___skimmed___ the paper for news about the concert. **(skim + ed)**

2. Matt never _____ a loaf of bread evenly. **(slice + s)**

3. Mom often _____ when she goes on a business trip. **(fly + es)**

4. Rachel has grown so tall that her skirt no longer _____. **(fit + s)**

5. Carla is always _____ her friends. **(tease + ing)**

6. It is _____ in the yard than on the porch. **(breezy + er)**

7. Chuck has more _____ than anyone I know. **(hobby + s)**

8. That table has a _____ surface than this one. **(flat + er)**

9. Your home computer is _____ than mine. **(new + er)**

10. This is the _____ glue I have ever used. **(sticky + est)**

11. The setting sun was _____ than the rising sun. **(red + er)**

12. Gilbert is in the garden _____ the hedges. **(clip + ing)**

13. The morning newspaper always has the _____ news. **(late + est)**

14. Fernando is _____ the bottles before returning them. **(empty + ing)**

15. Bumper is always _____ his tail. **(wag + ing)**

16. Julio lives in the _____ house in town. **(big + est)**

17. Tina's card shop is the _____ one to my house. **(close + est)**

18. Roger needs three _____ of this letter by tomorrow. **(copy + s)**

Read each sentence. Circle the word that completes the sentence. Then write the word on the line.

1. Alexis uses small ___brushes___ on her short curly hair. brush (brushes)

2. The Statue of Liberty holds a _____ in her right hand. torch torches

3. Sofia saw four _____ flying overhead. goose geese

4. The winner was smothered with _____ by her fans. kiss kisses

5. There are twelve inches in every _____. foot feet

6. The spirited hounds found the scent of three _____. fox foxes

7. A big cargo ship is docking at the long _____. wharf wharves

8. I was awakened by _____ scurrying across the floor. mouse mice

9. Cam bought two _____ for her mother and aunt. scarf scarves

Look at each picture. Then read the sentence. Circle the word that completes the sentence. Then write the word on the line.

1. The ___visitors'___ suitcases are in the lobby. visitor's visitors'

2. A _____ sound was heard outside the hall. trumpet's trumpets'

3. Look at the _____ mother guarding her family. kitten's kittens'

4. Pam always discards _____ rough outer leaves. lettuce's lettuces'

A suffix is a word part that is added to the end of a word. It changes the meaning of the word.

The suffix **ful** means **full of.** (skill**ful**)
The suffix **less** means **without.** (taste**less**)
The suffix **er** can mean **a person who.** (perform**er**)
The suffix **ness** can mean **condition** or **state of being.** (ill**ness**)
The suffix **y** can mean **having.** (luck**y**)
The suffix **ly** can mean **in a certain way.** (usual**ly**)

Read each meaning below. Add the suffix **ful, less, er, ness, y** or **ly** to each word shown in heavy type. Then write the word on the line. You may need to make spelling changes.

1. having **luck** _lucky_

2. without **care** _____

3. full of **color** _____

4. one who **dances** _____

5. without **motion** _____

6. being **soft** _____

7. one who **mines** _____

8. full of **harm** _____

9. in a **slow** way _____

10. in a **quiet** way _____

11. having **wealth** _____

12. being **hard** _____

13. being **dark** _____

14. one who **bakes** _____

15. full of **cheer** _____

16. having **health** _____

17. one who **wrestles** _____

18. without **life** _____

19. in a **proud** way _____

20. having **speed** _____

21. being **bright** _____

22. in a **kind** way _____

23. full of **flavor** _____

24. full of **skill** _____

25. having **room** _____

26. without **taste** _____

27. without **worth** _____

28. in a **usual** way _____

Read each sentence. Add the suffix **ful**, **less**, **er**, **ness**, **y**, or **ly** to each word to complete the sentence. Then write the word on the line. You may need to make spelling changes.

1. The carpenters completed their work neatly and ___quickly___. **quick**

2. A pie baked with fresh fruit is very _____. **flavor**

3. The gray room was dull and _____. **color**

4. A _____ left his packages on the counter. **shop**

5. "The _____ of the mattress is good for my back," said Mom. **firm**

6. Eating lots of fruit and vegetables makes me _____. **health**

7. Dad _____ takes us to soccer practice on Saturday. **usual**

8. It is hard to read in a _____ lit room. **dim**

9. I hope Annie will send a _____ reply to my letter. **speed**

10. Joey's _____ kept him out of school for two weeks. **ill**

11. The _____ took three bows at the end of the show. **perform**

12. Food cooked too long is often _____. **taste**

13. My dad is as _____ a cook as my mom. **skill**

14. A _____ chef doesn't waste an ounce of food. **care**

15. Gloria is studying music so she can become a _____. **sing**

16. The _____ in my toes was caused by the extreme cold. **numb**

17. Clara didn't finish her soup because it was too _____. **salt**

18. Daily exercise is part of our physical _____ program. **fit**

A suffix is a word part that is added to the end of a word. It changes the meaning of the word.

The suffix **ion** means **act of** or **thing that is**.
The suffix **ment** means **act, state,** or **result of being** or **doing**.

collec**tion**   agree**ment**

Read each sentence. Add the suffix **ion** or **ment** to each word to complete the sentence. Then write the word on the line.

1. The ___movement___ of the snail across the yard was very slow. **move**

2. _____ of the new gym will start next week. **Construct**

3. Chico wants to ride the roller coaster at the _____ park. **amuse**

4. Citizens vote in an _____ for president. **elect**

5. The bank sends my parents a _____ every month. **state**

6. Robin's _____ will be made final by the court. **adopt**

7. Jay makes a car _____ every other week. **pay**

8. Thomas Edison was responsible for the _____ of the light bulb. **invent**

9. This is an exciting spy story filled with lots of _____. **act**

10. Our choir is under the _____ of Mr. Shultz. **direct**

11. The _____ of citrus fruit will arrive tomorrow. **ship**

12. The lions were the main _____ at the circus. **attract**

13. The fire chief makes a yearly _____ of our school. **inspect**

14. My teacher has not seen any _____ in my dancing. **improve**

15. A _____ protects the rights of its people. **govern**

16. Bill and Jim made an _____ to join the club. **agree**

17. Nancy has to make one more _____ in her report. **correct**

18. José has a four o'clock _____ for a haircut. **appoint**

A suffix is a word part that is added to the end of a word. It changes the meaning of the word.

The suffix **ist** means **a person who.**
The suffix **ish** means **somewhat like.**

art**ist**   fool**ish**

Read each sentence. Add the suffix **ist** or **ish** to each word to complete the sentence. Then write the word on the line. You may need to make spelling changes.

1. A _____tourist_____ left his camera on the bus. **tour**

2. Lisa's coat is a light _____ color. **brown**

3. That _____ can work with paint, oil, and charcoal. **art**

4. The _____ sang his song alone on stage. **solo**

5. Brad's impolite behavior is very _____. **child**

6. Kim practices playing the violin so she can become a _____. **violin**

7. It was _____ of me to spend so much time at the zoo. **fool**

8. Armando is very pale and _____. **fever**

9. The _____ skillfully ran the new equipment. **machine**

10. A _____ writes long stories about imaginary people. **novel**

11. My mom is a _____ for our local paper. **journal**

12. Jason likes the _____ who draws those funny animals. **cartoon**

13. Dad's short haircut makes him look very _____. **boy**

14. Everyone noticed the _____ grin on Kevin's face. **elf**

15. James is a good _____ who never makes mistakes. **type**

16. The faded blue curtains were now _____. **green**

17. Look at the _____ waving to people on the ground. **balloon**

18. His _____ behavior is disturbing those around him. **clown**

> A suffix is a word part that is added to the end of a word. It changes the meaning of the word.
>
> The suffix **ous** means **full of.**
> The suffix **able** means **capable** or **worthy of being.**
>
> danger**ous**   depend**able**

Read each sentence. Add the suffix **ous** or **able** to each word to complete the sentence. Then write the word on the line. If a word ends in a silent **e,** remember to drop the **e** before adding **ous** or **able.**

1. This game looks as if it will be very __enjoyable__. **enjoy**

2. The miner struck gold in a very _____ place. **mountain**

3. Many accidents are _____ if people are careful. **avoid**

4. Hector is _____ because he is a swimming champion. **fame**

5. This old shopping cart is the only one _____. **avail**

6. With modern medicine, many diseases are _____. **cure**

7. I do not go near those snakes because their venom is _____. **poison**

8. Anita did not think the movie was very _____. **humor**

9. Deirdre put her _____ necklace in a safe place. **value**

10. Does a movie star lead a very _____ life? **glamor**

11. After my jacket is mended, will it be _____? **wear**

12. The people in that movie seem real and _____. **believe**

13. The hikers went on a _____ climb up the mountain. **peril**

14. The spot will come out because the blanket is _____. **wash**

15. Robin was _____ about singing on stage by herself. **nerve**

16. Tennis rackets come in _____ sizes and weights. **vary**

17. The wedding was a happy and _____ event. **joy**

18. Will this dress be _____ to wear to a wedding? **suit**

> A suffix is a word part that is added to the end of a word. It changes the meaning of the word.
>
> The suffix **al** means of or **relating to.**
> The suffix **ward** means **in the direction of.**
>
> ornament**al**   down**ward**

Read each sentence. Add the suffix **al** or **ward** to each word to complete the sentence. Then write the word on the line. You may need to make spelling changes.

1. There are many ___national___ parks across our country. **nation**

2. Fierce winds are blowing the fire _____. **east**

3. The violinist has outstanding _____ talent. **music**

4. It is _____ for rivers to flood in the spring. **nature**

5. Let's start walking _____ the park's exit. **to**

6. Jobs are often available in large _____ cities. **industry**

7. The tired travelers were _____ bound. **home**

8. The storm was moving _____ into colder regions. **north**

9. Both basement doors open _____. **out**

10. The plane's _____ is scheduled for 10:00 A.M. today. **arrive**

11. Adam glanced _____ before stepping into the taxi. **back**

12. Rachel learns a lot from television's _____ shows. **education**

13. The compass needle is pointing _____. **west**

14. Football is a _____ sport, usually played in the fall. **season**

15. Carmen looked _____ before getting into the glass elevator. **up**

16. Circus clowns are _____ and amusing. **comic**

17. Tako has her own _____ opinion about the celebration. **person**

18. _____ waves are caused by earthquakes on the ocean's floor. **Tide**

Read each sentence. Add the suffix **ful, less, er, ness, y, ly, ion, ment, ist, ish, ous, able, al,** or **ward** to each word to complete the sentence. Then write the word on the line. You may need to make spelling changes.

1. Without warning, the lights _suddenly_ went out. **(sudden + ly)**

2. Look at your _____ in the mirror! **(reflect + ion)**

3. More cement is needed to fix the cracked _____. **(pave + ment)**

4. We need Mr. Ruiz's _____ to go to the library. **(approve + al)**

5. Loren is so _____ that he only thinks of himself. **(self + ish)**

6. Chita's frisky little kitten is very _____. **(play + ful)**

7. It is _____ to ride a bike on that busy street. **(hazard + ous)**

8. With new batteries, this old radio will be _____ again. **(use + able)**

9. Fresh fruits and vegetables are _____. **(perish + able)**

10. Have you ever been a _____ on a television game show? **(panel + ist)**

11. If it is hot, Nina will wear a _____ shirt. **(sleeve + less)**

12. The hair _____ gave Natalia a very short haircut. **(style + ist)**

13. Our plumber didn't have the right _____ to fix the sink. **(equip + ment)**

14. Hal's _____ helped him win the chess game. **(clever + ness)**

15. The actor's _____ of Abe Lincoln was very believable. **(portray + al)**

16. Chuck's faded jeans now have a slightly _____ color. **(blue + ish)**

17. The cost of food is still rising _____. **(up + ward)**

18. Ellen will not eat food that is salty or _____. **(grease + y)**

Say each word listed below. Listen for the syllables in each word.
Then write each word on the line, drawing a slash between each syllable.

1. flavorful   fla/vor/ful   2. tourist   _____

3. government   _____   4. skillful   _____

5. westward   _____   6. hardness   _____

7. clownish   _____   8. personal   _____

9. roomy   _____   10. performer   _____

11. poisonous   _____   12. backward   _____

13. movement   _____   14. tasteless   _____

15. darkness   _____   16. healthy   _____

17. dangerous   _____   18. feverish   _____

19. proudly   _____   20. braveness   _____

21. brownish   _____   22. mountainous   _____

23. planter   _____   24. agreement   _____

25. cartoonist   _____   26. organist   _____

27. thoughtful   _____   28. foolish   _____

29. colorless   _____   30. banker   _____

31. firmness   _____   32. appointment   _____

33. pavement   _____   34. journalist   _____

35. teacher   _____   36. perilous   _____

37. amusement   _____   38. homeward   _____

39. seasonal   _____   40. arrangement   _____

41. hazardous   _____   42. numbness   _____

REVIEW Syllables and suffixes

Add the ending to each word listed below. Then write the word on the line. You may need to make spelling changes.

1. planet + s _____

2. skim + ed _____

3. ugly + er _____

4. delay + s _____

5. explore + ed _____

6. long + er _____

7. hot + er _____

8. jog + ing _____

9. party + es _____

10. victory + es _____

11. slice + ing _____

12. reply + es _____

13. wrap + s _____

14. dull + er _____

15. ostrich + es _____

16. hop + ed _____

17. close + est _____

18. thin + est _____

19. noisy + er _____

20. knife + es _____

21. hope + s _____

22. damage + ing _____

23. wolf + es _____

24. gray + er _____

25. empty + ed _____

26. country + es _____

27. late + er _____

28. reply + ing _____

29. jog + s _____

30. plan + ed _____

31. slip + ing _____

32. deny + es _____

33. clip + ed _____

34. examine + ing _____

35. near + est _____

36. puppy + es _____

37. compare + s _____

38. elf + es _____

39. safe + er _____

40. bury + es _____

Read each sentence. Circle the word that completes the sentence. Then write the word on the line.

1. Suki hung the new picture _____ on the wall. **arange**
   arrangement

2. An _____ reminds me of a piano. **organ**
   organist

3. Daniel was _____ and shared his lunch with Paula. **thought**
   thoughtful

4. The scouts found the _____ new hive in the garden. **bees**
   bees'

5. _____ brakes were responsible for the car crash. **Fault**
   Faulty

6. Let's _____ the causes of air pollution. **discuss**
   discussion

7. The _____ blue hat matched her blue coat. **woman's**
   women's

8. The roads were not _____ until the snowplow came. **pass**
   passable

9. Early pioneers moved _____ across the open plains. **west**
   westward

10. Mom is a good driver; she has never had an _____. **accident**
    accidental

11. Michael thinks _____ grapes are easier to eat. **seed**
    seedless

12. Everyone was amazed at how _____ the warrior was. **brave**
    braveness

13. The radio does not work because of a loose wire _____. **connect**
    connection

14. "Tap dancing in sneakers is _____," said Allen. **ridicule**
    ridiculous

15. David felt _____ in that silly chicken costume. **fool**
    foolish

16. Your apology is _____ to all of us. **accept**
    acceptable

17. It is _____ to cross a street when the light is red. **wrong**
    wrongly

18. The bank _____ was counting money in the vault. **tell**
    teller

TEST Inflectional endings and suffixes

A prefix is a word part that is added to the beginning of a word. It changes the meaning of the word.

The prefix **re** means **again.** (**re**appear)
The prefix **un** means **not,** or **opposite of.** (**un**kind)
The prefix **dis** means **not,** or **opposite of.** (**dis**appear)
The prefix **mid** means **middle,** or **half of.** (**mid**night)

Read each meaning below. Add the prefix **re, un, dis,** or **mid** to each word shown in heavy type. Then write the word on the line.

1. opposite of **happy** _unhappy_

2. **fill** again _____

3. **arrange** again _____

4. middle of a **stream** _____

5. not **honest** _____

6. not **true** _____

7. middle of **winter** _____

8. **do** again _____

9. **order** again _____

10. middle of the **day** _____

11. half **way** _____

12. not **able** _____

13. not **qualify** _____

14. **fuel** again _____

15. opposite of **buckle** _____

16. not **approve** _____

17. **build** again _____

18. middle of the **night** _____

19. not **pleased** _____

20. **capture** again _____

Read each word listed below. Circle the prefix. Then draw a line from each word to the phrase that tells what the word means.

(re)view	not happy or content
midday	go over or study again
unpleasant	not pleasing
discontent	noontime, middle of the day
return	middle of the week
midweek	opposite of connect or join together
disconnect	turn back again
unusual	tell positively again
repeat	not normal or typical

Complete each sentence by choosing a word from the box. Then write
the word on the line.

dissimilar	unbuckle	reappear	unspoiled	unhappy	respell
midwinter	disorganized	reclaimed	dishonest	unpleasant	refuel
disapprove	disqualify	returns	midnight	reorder	midstream

1. After the plane lands, passengers may __unbuckle__ their seat belts.

2. Mark's height will not _____ him from the basketball team.

3. When the waiter _____ to our table, Suki will order another salad.

4. If you know baseball, you know that stealing bases is not _____.

5. Dad said that the biggest fish are found _____.

6. My cat likes to disappear through the window only to _____ at the door.

7. "Don't be _____ that your present is the wrong size," said Grandmother.

8. "I can _____ the shirt in another size," responded Grandmother.

9. Carla _____ her lost puppy at the dog pound.

10. The judge asked the contestant to _____ the word "dictionary."

11. The little town was _____ by traffic and air pollution.

12. January and February are _____ months in North America.

13. Green and orange are _____ colors.

14. Having a sore throat can be very _____.

15. One second after _____ is the beginning of a new day.

16. Neighbors _____ of our having a goat in our back yard.

17. The trip was not fun because the leader was so _____.

18. Let's stop at that gas station to _____ the car.

Prefixes **re**, **un**, **dis**, and **mid**

> A prefix is a word part that is added to the beginning of a word. It changes the meaning of the word.
>
> The prefix **pre** means **before,** or **ahead of time.** (**pre**heat)
> The prefix **post** means **after,** or **later.** (**post**game)
> The prefix **uni** means **having one,** or **the same.** (**uni**cycle)
> The prefix **bi** means **having two,** or **happening every two.** (**bi**cycle)
> The prefix **tri** means **having three,** or **three times.** (**tri**cycle)

Read each meaning below. Add the prefix **pre, post, uni, bi,** or **tri** to each word shown in heavy type. Then write the word on the line.

1. having three **colors** ___tricolor___

2. **judge** ahead of time _____

3. having three **angles** _____

4. every three **months** _____

5. **view** ahead of time _____

6. a two-winged **plane** _____

7. **pay** ahead of time _____

8. **arrange** ahead of time _____

9. **date** later _____

10. **heat** ahead of time _____

11. before a **game** _____

12. after a **game** _____

13. before a thing is **mature** _____

14. before a **war** _____

15. after a **war** _____

16. every two **months** _____

Read each sentence. Circle the word that completes the sentence. Then write the word on the line.

1. The company will deliver only ___prepaid___ orders. (**prepaid**) **premature**

2. Every two weeks John has his _____ guitar lesson. **biweekly triweekly**

3. At the circus, animals ride their one-wheel _____. **unicycles biplanes**

4. Lauren can fly a _____ airplane, a plane with three motors. **trimotor tricycle**

5. If our team wins, there will be a _____ party. **pregame postgame**

6. Mom will often _____ food a day before she needs it. **precook prejudge**

Read each letter. Choose a word from the box above each letter to
complete each sentence. Then write the word on the line.

| prehistoric preview postgame preschool pregame postponed precook prejudge |

Dear Will,

Before our first soccer game next Saturday, please come to a __pregame__

party at my house. Mom will _____ some food for us to eat at the game.

Coach Mullen will give us a _____ of what to expect from the other

team. She says we should not _____ the other team.

Rosie and Brian, who went to _____ with us, are on the other team. I

wonder if Rosie still has her collection of _____ animal cards. Let's

invite Rosie and Brian to a _____ party next week and find out!

Your friend,
Sandy

P.S. If you have time before the party, write and tell me what you have been doing. I

hope the game is not _____ because of rain!

| unicycle | bimonthly | tricycle | binoculars | biplane |
| triangle | unicorn | bicycles | tricolor | uniforms |

Dear Sandy,

Last week I went on my _____ visit to the Animal Circus. I used

_____ to watch a pilot fly a _____ and do tricks

overhead. He trailed a _____ banner behind him.

As the show began, three monkeys swung from a _____-shaped

trapeze. Then six black bears, in red _____, raced each other on ten-

speed _____. Next a clown rode a tiny _____. I liked

the _____ who balanced on the _____ without falling.

I cannot wait to see you at the party!

Your pal,
Will

Prefixes **pre, post, uni, bi,** and **tri**

A prefix is a word part that is added to the beginning of a word. It changes the meaning of the word.

The prefix **non** means **not**, or **opposite, lacking,** or **absence of.** (**non**sense)
The prefix **in** means **not.** (**in**visible)
The prefixes **ir, il,** and **im** mean **not,** or **the opposite of.**

Use **ir** in front of words beginning with **r.** (**ir**regular)
Use **il** in front of words beginning with **l.** (**il**legal)
Use **im** in front of words beginning with **m, b,** and **p.** (**im**patient)

Read each meaning below. Add the prefix **in, non, ir, il,** or **im** to each word shown in heavy type. Then write the word on the line.

1. not **correct** _____incorrect_____ 2. not **pure** _____

3. lacking **fat** _____ 4. not **active** _____

5. not **formal** _____ 6. not **definite** _____

7. not **metal** _____ 8. not a **smoker** _____

9. not **responsible** _____ 10. without a **stop** _____

11. not a **resident** _____ 12. not a **reader** _____

Read each word listed below. Circle the prefix. Then draw a line from each word to the phrase that tells what the word means.

(im)mature   not equal in weight, size, or amount
imbalance   firmly fixed, cannot be moved
illogical   not fully grown or mature
imperfect   not complete or perfect
immovable   showing poor reasoning, not logical

insincere   having mistakes, not correct or exact
inexact   pretending, not real or sincere
inseparable   cannot be parted or separated
irresistible   not accurate or precise in every detail
imprecise   hard to fight against, cannot be resisted

Complete each sentence by choosing a word from the box. Then write the word on the line.

nonstop	invalid	infrequent	nonfiction	impolite	incorrect
illegal	nonsense	indefinite	impatient	immovable	nonresident
inactive	nonsmoker	nonskid	inexpensive	nonfat	irregular

1. When Paul is on a diet, he drinks ____nonfat____ milk.

2. Rosemary gets nervous and _____ when people are late.

3. Do those shoes have _____ rubber soles?

4. Sue will always be a _____ because she doesn't like the smell of smoke.

5. In the winter, most animals are _____.

6. The enormous boulder in front of our house is _____.

7. Tom cannot get a pool pass in my town because he is a _____.

8. Clothes with an _____ shape are often on sale.

9. Marcy took a _____ flight from San Francisco to Miami.

10. Joel was thrilled with his mark because none of his answers was _____.

11. Carmen was silent because she was afraid of being _____.

12. A present that costs very little is _____.

13. Our teacher will not allow any _____ in class.

14. It is _____ to drive through a red light.

15. Do you like to read fiction or _____ books?

16. Our picnic plans are _____ because they are still changing.

17. Rain is an _____ treat in the desert.

18. Pat's library card expired two weeks ago and is now _____.

Read each meaning below. Choose one of the prefixes in the box and add it to the word shown in heavy type. Then write the word on the lline.

dis	un	mid	uni	tri	in	im
re	post	pre	bi	non	il	ir

1. having three **colors** ___tricolor___

2. having two wheels or **cycles** _____

3. **heat** before time _____

4. after the **season** _____

5. not **able** _____

6. not **passable** _____

7. middle **size** _____

8. after the **war** _____

9. not **regular** _____

10. not **equal** _____

11. opposite of **appear** _____

12. without a **stop** _____

13. **appear** again _____

14. not **formal** _____

15. not **mature** _____

16. not **complete** _____

17. having one wheel or **cycle** _____

18. opposite of **comfort** _____

19. middle of the **summer** _____

20. not **legal** _____

21. after the **date** _____

22. **order** again _____

23. **fill** again _____

24. not **probable** _____

25. not **responsible** _____

26. having three **cities** _____

27. two-winged **plane** _____

28. not **proper** _____

29. not **kind** _____

30. **cook** before _____

31. **arrange** ahead of time _____

32. **date** earlier than the present _____

33. opposite of **order** _____

34. not **content** _____

35. before the **season** _____

36. middle of the **day** _____

Read each sentence. Use meaning clues to choose the word that completes the sentence. Circle the word. Then write the word on the line.

1. How long will it take to ____rebuild____ Joe's broken go-cart? **build** (**rebuild**)

2. After our team won the trophy, we had a _____ party. **game** **postgame**

3. Running very fast may cause an _____ heartbeat. **regular** **irregular**

4. All Americans are _____ under the law. **equal** **unequal**

5. Mom asked Danny to _____ the toys neatly. **arrange** **prearrange**

6. My parents always stay up until _____ on New Year's Eve. **night** **midnight**

7. It is _____ to park in front of a fire hydrant. **legal** **illegal**

8. Roberto is always _____ and courteous. **polite** **impolite**

9. Frank let the oven _____ while he prepared the fish. **heat** **preheat**

10. The _____ flag is red, white, and blue. **color** **tricolor**

11. If the water is _____, you should not drink it. **pure** **impure**

12. Jay cannot balance himself on a _____. **unicycle** **tricycle**

13. I finished my water, but the waiter will _____ my glass. **fill** **refill**

14. Bobby was happy that none of his answers was _____. **correct** **incorrect**

15. When Jim talks about skiing, he talks _____. **stop** **nonstop**

16. Did you take the training wheels off your _____? **cycle** **bicycle.**

17. My room is always messy and _____. **organized** **disorganized**

18. Kansas is _____ between Virginia and California. **midway** **way**

A prefix is a word part that is added to the beginning of a word. It changes the meaning of the word.

The prefix **mis** means **badly, incorrectly** or **lack of.** (**mis**place)
The prefix **co** means **with, together, jointly,** or **equally.** (**co**operate)
The prefix **over** means **above, higher than, more than,** or **too big.** (**over**eat)
The prefix **en** can mean **in, on, into, put into, give,** or **get.** (**en**danger)

Read each meaning below. Add the prefix **mis, co, over,** or **en** to each word shown in heavy type. Then write the word on the line.

1. **pronounce** wrong mispronounce

2. through the **night** _____

3. put into a **circle** _____

4. **treat** badly _____

5. lack of **trust** _____

6. **spell** incorrectly _____

7. **star** together _____

8. **pilot** together _____

9. **direct** incorrectly _____

10. **judge** incorrectly _____

11. **heat** beyond _____

12. **print** incorrectly _____

13. catch in a **trap** _____

14. **behave** badly _____

15. **fit** badly _____

16. **sleep** longer than planned _____

17. put into **force** _____

18. too big a **load** _____

Read each sentence. Circle the word that completes the sentence. Then write the word on the line.

1. Pat could not find the letter because it was ____misfiled____.   misuse
   (misfiled)

2. The huge machine was _____.   immovable
   insincere

3. Chris _____ the magazine on the newspaper rack.   misplaced
   mistrust

4. The _____ leader caused confusion.   illegal
   irresponsible

5. Winning a football game requires team _____.   cooperation
   coincidence

Read each paragraph. Choose a word from the box above each
paragraph to complete each sentence. Then write the word on the line.

misplace	coauthors	misbehave	misprints	entitled
cooperate	misspell	misfit	mispronouncing	mislabled

Marvin and Elizabeth are __coauthors__ of a book _____ "How

to Do Well in School." It tells pupils not to _____ or bother their
classmates. The rules in the book are easy to remember:

"Never _____ words in a written report."

"Avoid _____ words when reading out loud."

"Do not _____ homework papers or assignments."

"Always _____ with your teachers and friends."
Marvin and Elizabeth promise that if you follow their suggestions, you will not feel

like a _____ or be _____ a troublemaker.

"But don't blame us for any _____ in our book," says Elizabeth.
"We did our best to make the book accurate."

oversleep	overhand	misplace	misjudge	enjoy
overload	encourage	cooperate	enroll	overhear

Tomorrow is the day Fred will _____ in his new school, Forest Hills

School. He wonders if he will _____ this school as much as his last one.

Fred sets his alarm clock so he will not _____, but he worries and it is

hard for him to fall asleep. Will they _____ him with work? Will

he _____ his locker number? Will he _____ the other

pupils making fun of him? Will they _____ him?

Before he leaves for school in the morning, Fred's parents _____

him to _____ with his teachers and to make new friends. Fred hopes
he'll be happy at the new school. Maybe the school's ball team can use

his _____ pitching!

Prefixes **mis, co, over,** and **en**

> A prefix is a word part that is added to the beginning of a word.
> It changes the meaning of the word.
>
> The prefix **inter** means **between** or **among**. (**inter**lock)
> The prefix **mal** means **bad, badly,** or **fails to.** (**mal**treat)
> The prefix **semi** means **half, partly,** or **twice.** (**semi**sweet)
> The prefix **sub** means **under, below, lower** or **less than.** (**sub**way)

Read each meaning below. Add the prefix **inter, mal, semi,** or **sub** to each word shown in heavy type. Then write the word on the line.

1. partly **skilled** _semiskilled_   2. badly **adjusted** _____

3. failure to **function** _____   4. twice **weekly** _____

5. half a **circle** _____   6. badly **nourished** _____

7. **soil** below ground _____   8. partly **precious** _____

9. between **states** _____   10. **act** together or between _____

11. badly **formed** _____   12. partly **dark** _____

13. outside an **urban** area _____   14. **weave** among _____

Read each word listed below. Circle the prefix. Then draw a line from each word to the phrase that tells what the word means.

(sub)title — partly sweet

maltreat — beneath the main title

semisweet — treat badly

subway — passageway underground

substandard — less than the final total

subtotal — partly tropical

semitropical — below standard

subbasement — floor beneath the basement

Read the paragraph. Choose a word from the box to complete each sentence. Then write the word on the line.

malnourished	interact	semiweekly	interplanetary
malfunction	semifinal	interchange	semisweet

In this episode of "Astronauts in Space," Kelly and Roger are trying to repair a **malfunction** in their rocket engine. They fear that their _____ trip from Earth to Mars will be over if they don't _____ the bad engine parts with good ones. The explorers _____ well together, but they are getting tired and hungry.

"I feel so _____. I wish I had a sandwich and some cookies with _____ chocolate chips to eat," says Kelly.

"I wish I were home watching the _____ round of the basketball tournament," says Roger.

Will Kelly and Roger make it? Watch our _____ show to find out!

Read each sentence. Circle the word that completes the sentence. Then write the word on the line.

1. Let's go to the theater lobby during **intermission**. (intermission) interrupt

2. The pupils are sitting in a _____. **semicircle** semiskilled

3. In a city, people often travel on a _____. **subway** **submarine**

4. _____ travel may soon be very common. **Interplanetary** **International**

5. The pieces of a jigsaw puzzle _____. **interact** **interlock**

6. A _____ car gets good mileage and is inexpensive. **subcompact** **substation**

Prefixes **inter, mal, semi,** and **sub**

Read each sentence. Use meaning clues to choose the word that completes the sentence. Circle the word. Then write the word on the line.

1. Rose knew she did not _misspell_ "giraffe" on the test.   spell (misspell)

2. Gerry took the lost, _____ dog to the animal shelter.   nourished **malnourished**

3. We saw the river below as we walked across the _____.   pass **overpass**

4. Nick decided to _____ the model plane on the bookcase.   place **misplace**

5. The _____ of a book is not as important as its main title.   title **subtitle**

6. The dancers from Ireland won the _____ prize.   national **international**

7. A _____ helps the captain fly the airplane.   pilot **copilot**

8. Jill bought some very _____ pineapple for her friend.   sweet **semisweet**

9. The river is about to _____ its banks.   flow **overflow**

10. Brian certainly knows how to _____ a good laugh.   joy **enjoy**

11. The test directions tell you to _____ the correct answer.   circle **semicircle**

12. A diamond is a very _____ stone.   precious **semiprecious**

13. Sandy and Tim are _____ employed in different companies.   workers **coworkers**

14. Coaches always _____ players to get enough rest.   courage **encourage**

15. If the engines _____ properly, the plane will land on time.   function **malfunctioning**

16. Emily went to visit Carol and will stay there _____.   night **overnight**

17. The _____ highway runs from Maine through Florida.   state **interstate**

18. A dictionary tells you how to _____ new words.   pronounce **mispronounce**

Say each word listed below. Listen for the syllables in each word.
Then write each word in syllables on the line.

1. unbutton   un but ton _____

2. improper _____

3. imperfect _____

4. tricolor _____

5. nonskid _____

6. entrap _____

7. bimonthly _____

8. subway _____

9. enforce _____

10. incorrect _____

11. midsummer _____

12. biplane _____

13. informal _____

14. nonstop _____

15. misbehave _____

16. enroll _____

17. coworker _____

18. discontent _____

19. mistreat _____

20. postdate _____

21. preschool _____

22. illegal _____

23. postgame _____

24. enjoy _____

25. malform _____

26. endanger _____

27. subsoil _____

28. preview _____

29. midday _____

30. nonfat _____

31. unequal _____

32. prejudge _____

33. dishonor _____

34. nonmetal _____

35. rebuild _____

36. improve _____

37. unhappy _____

38. nonreader _____

39. midair _____

40. impolite _____

Add the prefix to each word listed below. Then write the word and its meaning on the lines.

1. un + true _____ _____

2. re + fill _____ _____

3. dis + honest _____ _____

4. over + sleep _____ _____

5. mid + stream _____ _____

6. sub + way _____ _____

7. in + doors _____ _____

8. mis + spell _____ _____

9. pre + season _____ _____

10. co + worker _____ _____

11. ir + regular _____ _____

12. mis + treat _____ _____

13. im + patient _____ _____

Complete each sentence by choosing a word from above. Then write the word on the line. You will not use all the words listed above.

1. When Maria was sick, the druggist had to _____ her prescription twice.

2. It is _____ that all flowers are yellow.

3. Theresa didn't want to _____ on the day she was going to start camp.

4. Daniel does not like to see anyone _____ an animal.

5. Amanda is the best _____ I've ever had.

6. Dwayne was _____ for the start of summmer vacation.

7. The store clerk who gave Jennifer the wrong change was _____.

8. Russell was careful not to _____ "neighbor" on the test.

Read each sentence. Use meaning clues to choose the word that
completes the sentence. Circle the word. Then write the word on the
line.

1. Michelle believes in _____ rights for all people. **equal**
   unequal

2. Juan will _____ his sand castle after the wave hits. **build**
   rebuild

3. It is Ivan's turn to _____ the rules in the lunchroom. **force**
   enforce

4. Wendy carved a _____ for a nose on her pumpkin. **angle**
   triangle

5. The children took a ten-mile _____ trip last week. **cycle**
   bicycle

6. We will have a _____ party the day after the last game. **season**
   postseason

7. Dad will _____ of my glowing report card. **approve**
   disapprove

8. Jeff wanted the surprise present for his father to be _____. **perfect**
   imperfect

9. The astronauts fixed the _____ in the rocket. **function**
   malfunction

10. Did the water in your bathtub _____ onto the floor? **flow**
    overflow

11. We always enjoy the _____ picnic on July 4th. **annual**
    semiannual

12. Let's _____ some chicken soup to eat right now. **cook**
    precook

13. Kim avoids the hot _____ sun in summer. **day**
    midday

14. Amy moved to Canton, Ohio, and became a _____ there. **resident**
    nonresident

15. Pete and Al always _____ and finish their chores on time. **operate**
    cooperate

16. Debby took the _____ highway from Ohio to Pennsylvania. **state**
    interstate

17. Suzy loves her pet parrot and _____ it kindly. **treats**
    mistreats

18. It is _____ to drive a car without a license. **legal**
    illegal

TEST Prefixes

A contraction is formed when two words are put together with one or more letters left out. An apostrophe, the mark ', is used in place of the missing letter or letters. The new word is shorter, but its meaning is the same.

was + not—wasn't
can + not—can't   where + is—where's

Draw lines in each box from each pair of words to the contraction the words form.

1.		2.		3.	
it + is	she's	had + not	wouldn't	is + not	aren't
should + not	it's	did + not	who's	are + not	hasn't
were + not	weren't	would + not	hadn't	does + not	he's
she + is	shouldn't	who + is	didn't	there + is	there's
do + not	haven't	will + not	mustn't	he + is	isn't
have + not	couldn't	what + is	won't	that + is	doesn't
could + not	don't	must + not	what's	has + not	that's

Read each sentence. Circle the word that completes the sentence. Then write the word on the line.

1. Kim and Maria __didn't__ bring their lunch with them today. **don't** (**didn't**)

2. Do you think _____ a better skater than I am? **she's it's**

3. Look! _____ a zebra with all the stripes! **There's What's**

4. My friends Peter and Lynn _____ swim in deep water. **isn't can't**

5. Luis _____ go on the new roller coaster with me. **haven't won't**

6. _____ my turn to use the new paint brushes. **It's What's**

7. _____ going to help us wash the windows in the den? **Who's There's**

8. Our school bus driver _____ wait for anyone who is late. **haven't doesn't**

9. There _____ any room in the closet for your new suit. **mustn't isn't**

10. People _____ drive fast on wet roads or steep hills. **wasn't shouldn't**

11. _____ the wrong shirt to wear with a dark blue suit. **That's There's**

12. Angela woke up late and _____ get to practice on time. **hadn't couldn't**

Read the letter that Raul wrote to his friend Eli. Circle the words in the letter that can be put together to form **n't** and **'s** contractions. Then write the contractions on the lines below the letter.

Dear Eli,

(It is) so wonderful here in the country. There is a chestnut horse living at the next farm. It is a beauty! How I would like to ride that horse before the summer is over. However, there is something funny going on here at camp. I was awake late last night. I know I should not have been awake, but I was. I heard a lot of noise outside my window. I looked out of my window and could not help noticing a porcupine. "What is a porcupine doing up in the weeping willow tree?" I asked myself. To my surprise, it is slowly eating all the branches of the tree. Nevertheless, it is a real noisy pest, but I cannot help laughing at it. Luckily, it has not seen me watching it. So it will be back tomorrow night. That is my adventure story for this week.

Are you not coming to visit soon? I have not heard from anyone back home. Do not forget to write.

Your friend,
Raul

It's

Contractions **n't** and **'s**

> A contraction is formed when two words are put together with one or more letters left out. An apostrophe, the mark ', is used in place of the missing letter or letters. The new word is shorter, but its meaning is the same.
>
> it + will—it'll   they + would—they'd
> I + had—I'd

Draw lines in each box from each pair of words to the contraction the words form.

1.		**2.**		**3.**	
he + will	we'll	I + will	she'll	they + had	they'd
you + would	he'll	we + would	I'd	who + would	she'd
we + will	we'd	they + will	they'll	I + would	you'd
we + had	he'd	he + had	we'd	you + had	I'd
she + had	she'd	she + will	I'll	she + would	you'll
he + would	you'd	I + had	he'd	you + will	who'd

Read each sentence. Circle the word that completes the sentence. Then write the word on the line.

1. They said _they'd_ be here for dinner before eight o'clock.   I'll (they'd)

2. After school, _____ help you carry those big boxes and cartons.   **who'd I'll**

3. Without help, _____ never learn that speech.   **he'd it'll**

4. _____ come to my party on Sunday, won't you?   **You'll I'd**

5. _____ have thought we'd lose the spelling bee?   **It'll Who'd**

6. Here's what _____ do if the sun comes out later today.   **we'll who'd**

7. _____ already left the house when I arrived.   **She'd I'll**

8. Please ask the players if _____ start practice now.   **they'll he'd**

9. _____ like to make a big splash in that rain puddle.   **Who'd I'd**

10. Do you think _____ join our art club?   **she'll we'd**

11. _____ be hard to fit your clothes in that suitcase.   **I'll It'll**

12. If you call Alan, _____ come over and study with you.   **she'll he'll**

13. If the lake freezes, _____ all like to go ice skating.   **we'd I'd**

Read the letter that Abby wrote to her friend Tracy. Circle the words in the letter that can be put together to form **'ll** and **'d** contractions. Then write the contractions on the lines below the letter.

Dear Tracy,

(It will) be no huge surprise to you that our cat finally had her kittens—all six of them. I would have written sooner, but it has been so busy here. You will have to see the charming little creatures . . . but quick. Our friends from across the street arrived and said they would like to take two of the kittens. Ms. Romero, my teacher, said she would like the frisky brown one. We had considered keeping two. So who would take the last one? You would love the white one with the light brown patch over each eye. She's active and does fantastic jumping tricks. Wouldn't you like having a pet of your own? Think about it.

What's new with you? There's something else I forgot to tell you. Our guppy, Sam, is about to have babies. So we will give her a new name—Samantha.

See you soon,
Abby

_____ It'll _____   _____   _____

_____   _____   _____

_____   _____   _____

NAME _____

> A contraction is formed when two words are put together with one or more letters left out. An apostrophe, the mark ', is used in place of the missing letter or letters. The new word is shorter, but its meaning is the same.
>
> you + are—you're   we + have—we've

Draw lines in each box from each pair of words to the contraction the words form.

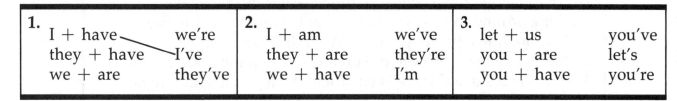

1.			2.			3.		
I + have		we're	I + am		we've	let + us		you've
they + have		I've	they + are		they're	you + are		let's
we + are		they've	we + have		I'm	you + have		you're

Read each sentence. Circle the word that completes the sentence. Then write the word on the line.

1. **They've** already started the one-mile race. We're (They've)

2. At 9 o'clock _____ always ready to go to bed. **we've I'm**

3. _____ the number one team in the country. **We're I'm**

4. _____ never been to Rhode Island or New York. **We've We're**

5. _____ been my best friend for a very long time. **I'm You've**

6. _____ packing our clothes for summer camp. **They've We're**

7. _____ my older cousins from New York City. **We're They're**

8. You'll be surprised to see all the shells _____ collected. **let's I've**

9. _____ go on a long hike up the mountain. **I'm Let's**

10. It looks like _____ about to begin the race. **they're I've**

11. John thinks _____ going to be on our ice hockey team. **you're let's**

12. Can you guess how many pancakes _____ made already? **you're I've**

13. If everyone is here, _____ begin to count the votes. **we're let's**

14. The skirt _____ wearing is very bright and colorful. **you're they've**

15. _____ a loyal fan of our high school baseball team. **I'm You'd**

Contractions 'm, 're, 've, and 's

Read the letter that Billie wrote to his friend Coco. Circle the words in the letter that can be put together to form **'m, 're, 've,** and **'s** contractions. Then write the contractions on the lines below the letter.

Dear Coco,

(I have) a hilarious tale to tell you. We have been going to the zoo almost every weekend. There is a friendly elephant there who always wails at us. It doesn't wail at everyone, but it'll wait until we stand near the rail and then start wailing. Well, that is how it all started. Who would have guessed what would happen next?

Try to picture this scene. The time is early morning. We are walking around the elephant area. I am standing next to my father, holding a bag of peanuts. We didn't expect it, but suddenly we were showered with a flood of water. What is this? We turn around and there is our friendly elephant standing near its drinking pool. We laughed until we thought we would burst. I guess that is how it shows its friendship. Anyway, it didn't seem to mind wet peanuts. I am hoping it won't try the same trick on you and me when we visit the zoo next week.

Let us talk on the telephone soon.

Your wet friend,
Billie

I've _____ _____ _____

_____ _____ _____ _____

_____ _____ _____ _____

Read each sentence. Put the words together to form a contraction.
Then write the contraction on the line.

1. ___I've___ never flown in an airplane or a jet. (I + have)

2. Christa and Mark will pick you up when _____ ready. (you + are)

3. _____ like to plan a picnic for the team. (We + would)

4. Mr. Rodriguez _____ know about his surprise party. (must + not)

5. _____ been sick for days before going to the doctor. (He + had)

6. We just _____ be late for the surprise birthday party. (can + not)

7. After _____ washed the windows, it began to rain. (we + had)

8. Do you think _____ going to snow this morning? (it + is)

9. _____ see if Mom is working in the garage. (I + will)

10. My teacher thought the scores _____ been higher. (could + have)

11. We _____ allowed to go out after 7 o'clock. (are + not)

12. _____ already left home when the bus came by the house. (They + had)

13. _____ ask if the twins are home so we can visit them. (Let + us)

14. Dad doesn't think _____ funny when I hide his shoes. (it + is)

15. _____ not going to softball practice after school. (I + am)

16. _____ already left for town when it started to rain. (I + had)

17. Dad said there _____ enough paint to finish the hall. (was + not)

18. This is the third time _____ won first prize. (you + have)

Read each sentence. Circle the words in the sentence that can be put together to form a contraction. Then write the contraction on the line.

1. I am a better tap dancer than ice skater.   _____

2. She is trying to find a new home for the lost kitten.   _____

3. You must not touch a hot stove or dish.   _____

4. Ask Josh if he will play outfield in the game today.   _____

5. Mom knew you would be hungry after your hike in the woods.   _____

6. Who is making all that noise out there?   _____

7. It is best to plant a flower garden in the early spring.   _____

8. The baby whale did not stay with the other whales.   _____

9. Where is the new roller skating rink?   _____

10. Let us find Australia on the wall map.   _____

11. You are the best player on our track team.   _____

12. We will be at the train station in 5 minutes.   _____

13. Who would like to be the first one to ride the camel?   _____

14. I have always wanted to climb that mountain.   _____

15. We should not have been playing the music so loud.   _____

16. Rosa will go to the tennis match if you will go, too.   _____

17. Sam does not want to go shopping with me today.   _____

18. We are going to do three errands for Dad.   _____

TEST Contractions **n't, 's, 'll, 'd, 'm, 're,** and **'ve**

Synonyms are words that are the same or almost the same in meaning.

shut   close   buy   purchase

Draw lines in the boxes between two words that have the same meaning.

1.		2.		3.	
part	glad	several	noise	entire	windy
nourish	tired	look	many	tasty	tired
weary	piece	sound	fresh	breezy	all
happy	feed	new	glance	drowsy	delicious

Choose a synonym for the underlined word. Then write the word on the line.

old	under	correct	point	sheet
unwise	trip	shy	look	construct

1. <u>build</u> a house   ___construct___ a house

2. an <u>ancient</u> wall   an _____ wall

3. such a <u>foolish</u> character   such an _____ character

4. ready to <u>search</u>   ready to _____

5. a long <u>journey</u>   a long _____

6. reach the <u>peak</u>   reach the _____

7. on that <u>page</u>   on that _____

8. a <u>right</u> answer   a _____ answer

9. <u>below</u> the bridge   _____ the bridge

10. a <u>bashful</u> child   a _____ child

Read each sentence. Circle the word that has the same meaning as the underlined word.

1. Did that contractor <u>build</u> this apartment building? **labor** (**construct**)

2. Look how the rain <u>glistens</u> in the sun. **sparkles** **strikes**

3. Jamie <u>owns</u> that hockey stick. **puts** **possesses**

4. Let's <u>climb</u> the rocky mountain. **pursue** **ascend**

5. Alicia's new party dress is <u>gorgeous</u>. **stingy** **beautiful**

6. The athlete had hot cereal and an egg that was <u>raw</u> for breakfast. **tasty** **uncooked**

7. Go <u>quickly</u> to warn the hikers that the bridge is washed out. **silently** **rapidly**

8. Be sure to <u>write</u> the speaker's exact words. **listen** **record**

9. Ling Ping <u>hurt</u> her knuckles playing soccer. **injured** **inflamed**

10. Amanda and Joel apologized for their <u>mistakes</u>. **accidents** **errors**

11. Trixie will be <u>secure</u> in our back yard. **safe** **leashed**

12. The babysitter will <u>remain</u> until Mr. and Mrs. Ortiz return home. **stay** **leave**

13. In the adventure story, the pilot showed her <u>bravery</u>. **determination** **courage**

14. Doctor Foster <u>inspected</u> the cut on Erica's foot. **examined** **touched**

15. It is <u>necessary</u> for Alexis to come to band practice. **fine** **required**

16. "<u>Halt</u>! You must show your pass card." **Stall** **Stop**

17. <u>Evening</u> comes quietly after sunset. **Silence** **Night**

18. My little sister was caught in the <u>revolving</u> door. **turning** **moving**

Synonyms

NAME _____

Read the story. For each underlined word, select a synonym from the box. Then write the synonym on the line below the story.

pursue	ray	sorrow	locate	noise
thought	sketch	tired	speeding	strength
dreary	changed	careful	shine	anxious

Alan was very worried.¹ Although he was cautious² while walking in the woods, his friend somehow became lost in the dismal³ forest. "It takes energy⁴ to hike back up the mountain," he said to himself. Would he find⁵ his friend in time? He wasn't sure. A feeling of great sadness⁶ came over him. Suddenly, Alan heard a sound.⁷ He altered⁸ his direction. "Follow⁹ that sound," he thought. Alan was growing weary.¹⁰ If only he had a drawing¹¹ of the area. Just then Alan saw something gleam.¹² "Could it be my friend?" he wondered.¹³ He called and soon Gappy came racing¹⁴ toward him. Fortunately, Alan had noticed a beam¹⁵ of sunlight on his dog's metal name tag.

1. __anxious__ 4. _____ 7. _____ 10. _____ 13. _____

2. _____ 5. _____ 8. _____ 11. _____ 14. _____

3. _____ 6. _____ 9. _____ 12. _____ 15. _____

Read the clues for the crossword puzzle. Choose a synonym for each clue from the words in the box. Then write the synonym to complete the puzzle.

ferocious	inform	split	nourish	dreary	assist	middle
handsome	handle	tender	destroy	during	vary	tie
frequently	funny	lead	inspect	entire	hasty	fool
terrible	insist	stun	fragment	shut	beat	unlock

Across

1. divide
2. fierce
3. dismal
4. touch
5. help
7. quick
9. change
10. open
12. often
15. feed
18. win
19. center
21. all
22. awful
23. demand

Down

1. daze
2. humorous
3. ruin
6. soft
7. attractive
8. bind
11. while
12. piece
13. trick
14. close
16. tell
17. examine
20. guide

Antonyms are words that are opposite in meaning.

beginning   ending   best   worst

Draw lines in the boxes between two words that have the opposite meaning.

1.		2.		3.	
bright	poor	slender	empty	walk	young
whisper	frown	glum	question	easy	run
rich	clean	answer	miss	short	wide
dirty	dull	hit	fat	old	tall
smile	shout	full	happy	narrow	difficult

Choose an antonym for the underlined word. Then write the word on the line.

correct	hates	crying	terrible	below
descend	late	thick	noisy	smooth

1. <u>ascend</u> the hill _____ **descend** _____ the hill

2. a <u>flat</u> pancake   a _____ pancake

3. a <u>wonderful</u> vacation   a _____ vacation

4. a <u>silent</u> park   a _____ park

5. <u>incorrect</u> spelling   _____ spelling

6. the <u>laughing</u> baby   the _____ baby

7. <u>above</u> our heads   _____ our heads

8. a <u>coarse</u> piece of paper   a _____ piece of paper

9. <u>early</u> in the day   _____ in the day

10. <u>loves</u> the pool   _____ the pool

Read each sentence. Circle the word that has the opposite meaning of
the underlined word.

1. Strong horses pulled the covered wagons. (Weak) Big

2. Dimitri dislikes sour plums. **purple   sweet**

3. The heroes of the story were strong and brave. **kind   cowardly**

4. Several men and women from Greece visited our school. **Many   Few**

5. Let's go indoors before it pours. **inside   outdoors**

6. Look and you will see the crest of the hill just ahead. **top   bottom**

7. Suki had great confidence in Chuck's ability. **trust   disbelief**

8. A gold necklace is a costly present. **much   cheap**

9. The point on Ron's pencil is dull. **flat   sharp**

10. Before we leave the house, let's count our money. **Early   After**

11. Kate was careful with the fragile glass pitcher. **kind   careless**

12. Be quiet or you'll keep the baby awake. **alert   asleep**

13. My brother Ivan is always sloppy. **messy   neat**

14. Martin disagrees with everything Otto says. **argues   agrees**

15. Maggie accepted the gift Jesse gave her. **took   rejected**

16. After a few days in bed, Kim felt better. **good   worse**

17. Edwin found a dead bird by the road. **live   rotted**

18. Please don't leave without taking me with you. **go   come**

Read the words in the box. Answer each riddle by choosing the word from the box that is an antonym for the underlined word. Then write the word on the line.

straight	inner	strong
empty	subtract	lowest

1. I am an antonym for <u>fragile</u> and I have six letters.

   What word am I? ___strong___

2. I have eight letters. I mean the opposite of <u>add</u>.

   What word am I? _____

3. I am an antonym for <u>outer</u> and I have five letters.

   What word am I? _____

4. I have eight letters. I mean the opposite of <u>crooked</u>.

   What word am I? _____

5. I am an antonym for <u>highest</u>. I have six letters.

   What word am I? _____

6. I have five letters. I mean the opposite of <u>full</u>.

   What word am I? _____

Read each pair of sentences. Then circle the words that are antonyms.

1. Marie was (chilled) by the wind.
   She went inside and was (warmed) by the fire.

2. Leave the stage after you've said your lines.
   Return to the stage for the final song.

3. In the morning Pedro felt very healthy.
   Later, however, he began feeling sick.

4. Anjoli's baby brother seemed to be sleepy.
   After his nap, he was alert again.

5. Those big red strawberries were fresh yesterday.
   How did they become spoiled overnight?

6. When diamonds are found in mines, they are very rough.
   Polished diamonds, however, are smooth and brilliant.

Read the clues for the crossword puzzle. For clues <u>across</u>, choose <u>antonyms</u> from the box. For clues <u>down</u>, choose <u>synonyms</u> from the box. Then write the antonyms and synonyms to complete the puzzle.

outside	often	sparkle	delicious	descend	poor	uncooked
fragile	real	open	unsafe	old	question	stay
cowardly	early	forest	love	injure	journey	alike
smooth	fat	look	empty	sloppy	noise	possess

Across

1. strong
4. late
5. safe
10. young
12. answer
13. rich
17. inside
18. bravely
21. hate
23. ascend
24. neat
25. rough

Down

2. true
3. hurt
4. vacant
6. glisten
7. woods
8. trip
9. raw
10. frequently
11. tasty
13. own
14. same
15. sound
16. remain
19. search
20. unlock
22. heavy

Synonyms and Antonyms

Homonyms are words that sound the same but have different meanings.

one   won   flower   flour

Draw lines in each box between two words that have the same sound.

1.		2.		3.	
cellar	not	site	tow	waist	night
close	seller	which	bury	knight	made
beach	vain	berry	weigh	maid	dough
knot	clothes	toe	sight	dew	waste
vane	beech	way	witch	doe	do

Choose a homonym for the underlined word. Then write the word on the line.

toad	sum	knot	right	whale
fare	pane	stare	break	heard

1. <u>write</u> a letter   the ____right____ answer

2. go up a <u>stair</u>   _____ at someone

3. a <u>herd</u> of cattle   _____ a sound

4. <u>some</u> groceries   a _____ of money

5. <u>pain</u> in the leg   a _____ of glass

6. <u>not</u> happy   tie a _____

7. go to a <u>fair</u>   pay a _____

8. the <u>towed</u> car   the _____ jumped

9. put on the <u>brake</u>   _____ a glass

10. to cry and <u>wail</u>   a _____ in the ocean

Read each sentence. If the underlined word is correct, write **C** on the line. If the underlined word is not correct, cross out the incorrect word and write its homonym on the line.

1. I ate a <u>peace</u> of pie. _____piece_____

2. The climbers reached the <u>peak</u> of the mountain. _____

3. The gardener hammered the <u>steak</u> into the ground. _____

4. Please <u>clothes</u> the cupboard. _____

5. The doctor injected a needle into the patient's <u>vein</u>. _____

6. Kelly was <u>board</u> at the band concert. _____

7. The scale shows that my <u>wait</u> is 70 pounds. _____

8. Matthew's <u>father</u> drove by the park. _____

9. There is a <u>beech</u> tree in Grandmother's yard. _____

10. "<u>Witch</u> way is the museum?" asked the tourist. _____

11. The school bus was <u>toad</u> when it broke down. _____

12. The umpire's ruling was not <u>fair</u>. _____

13. Sir Lancelot was a <u>night</u> of the Round Table. _____

14. When our pet parakeet died, we decided to <u>berry</u> it. _____

15. The <u>roots</u> of that tree go under the street. _____

16. Della has <u>groan</u> two inches this year. _____

17. I wonder if my dog has <u>flees</u>. _____

18. The <u>seller</u> of the car would not lower the price. _____

19. The Tigers <u>one</u> the soccer game by three points. _____

20. <u>Their</u> isn't much snow left on the ground. _____

21. A tailor will <u>so</u> your ripped jacket. _____

NAME _____

Read the story. Choose the correct word from the pair of homonyms
under the line. Write the word on line.

The brown _____bear_____ is a huge animal. It can be
       (bare   bear)

_____ in parts of North America, Asia, and Europe. A
(seen   scene)

brown bear has gray, tan, or blonde _____.
          (hare   hair)

_____ special feature of this bear is the hump on its back.
(One   Won)

The diet of a brown bear is not unusual. Included in the diet is lots

of _____. The brown bear hunts _____ fish
   (meat   meet)   **(for   four)**

in rivers and lakes. Other favorite foods are _____ and
                      (buries   berries)

honey.

Bear cubs _____ climb trees; however, adult bears are
      (do   dew)

_____ heavy to climb trees. Most brown bears live
(too   two)

_____ themselves. When the _____ is cold,
(by   buy)   **(weather whether)**

they sleep in dens. During warmer seasons, they travel a long

_____ to find food.
(way   weigh)

Brown bears have _____ almost completely pushed out
          (bin   been)

of much of North America. _____, however, have found
           (Sum   Some)

homes in Canada and Alaska and continue to thrive

_____.
(there   their)

Read the clues for the crossword puzzle. Choose a homonym for each clue from the word in the box. Then write the homonym to complete the puzzle.

our	beach	stair	rose	weigh	flee	toe	which	sum
one	berry	clothes	seller	route	grown	fare	knight	not
waist	sew	board	dew	hair	weather	vein	mane	heard

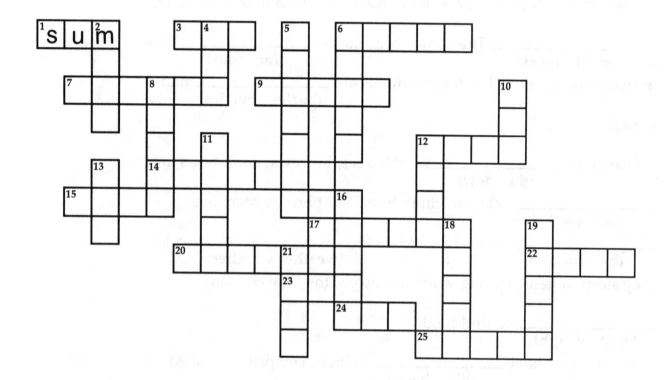

Across

1. some
3. won
6. beech
7. night
9. bored
12. flea
14. whether

15. vane
17. cellar
20. stare
22. hare
23. hour
24. due
25. way

Down

2. main
4. knot
5. close
6. bury
8. groan
10. tow
11. waste

12. fair
13. so
16. herd
18. root
19. witch
21. rows

Homonyms

Write a meaning for each of the following words. Then give an example of each one.

synonyms _____

antonyms _____

homonyms _____

From the box, select a synonym, antonym, or homonym for each word listed below. Then write the word on the line.

fare	early	knot	heard	cry
mane	root	miss	humorous	split
ahead	toad	ferocious	cowardly	cellar
love	attractive	wail	frequently	answer
break	ruin	happy	wonderful	

1. fierce   synonym   <u>ferocious</u>
2. route   homonym   _____
3. hate   antonym   _____
4. handsome   synonym   _____
5. towed   homonym   _____
6. late   antonym   _____
7. forward   synonym   _____
8. laugh   antonym   _____
9. not   homonym   _____
10. herd   homonym   _____
11. divide   synonym   _____
12. fair   homonym   _____

13. question   antonym   _____
14. glum   antonym   _____
15. brake   homonym   _____
16. destroy   synonym   _____
17. whale   homonym   _____
18. often   synonym   _____
19. terrible   antonym   _____
20. hit   antonym   _____
21. seller   homonym   _____
22. funny   synonym   _____
23. brave   antonym   _____
24. main   homonym   _____

Draw a line between each pair of synonyms, antonyms, and homonyms.

1. Synonyms		2. Antonyms		3. Homonyms	
vacant	attractive	neat	unsafe	knight	night
journey	empty	secure	cry	flea	beech
slender	trip	rough	smooth	rose	flee
handsome	thin	laugh	sloppy	beach	rows

For each pair of words, write **S** if the words are synonyms, **A** if they are antonyms, and **H** if they are homonyms.

1. write   record   —
2. cheap   expensive   —
3. dull   sharp   —
4. bury   berry   —
5. stay   remain   —
6. steak   stake   —
7. before   after   —
8. raw   uncooked   —
9. bravely   cowardly   —
10. wait   weight   —
11. indoors   outdoors   —
12. own   possess   —
13. peace   piece   —
14. error   mistake   —
15. careless   careful   —

16. hurt   injure   —
17. weak   strong   —
18. young   elderly   —
19. close   clothes   —
20. safe   unsafe   —
21. construct   build   —
22. worse   better   —
23. weather   whether   —
24. one   won   —
25. accept   reject   —
26. grown   groan   —
27. sparkle   glisten   —
28. come   leave   —
29. neat   sloppy   —
30. vane   vain   —

The words at the top of a dictionary page are called **guide words.** Guide words are used in many dictionaries. The first guide word tells you the first word on the page. The second guide word tells you the last word on the page.

The words on a dictionary page are listed in alphabetical order. To find a word, you may need to look at the second letter of each word. If the first and second letters in each word are the same, look at the third letter.

apple	bat	can
banana	bee	camp
carrot	bull	cave

Read the group of words in each box. Decide if you need to use the first, second, or third letter to put the words in alphabetical order. Then write the words in alphabetical order on the lines.

1.
diamond   _diamond_

pearl   _____

ruby   _____

emerald   _____

2.
elephant   _____

eel   _____

eagle   _____

ermine   _____

3.
shield   _____

shamrock   _____

sheep   _____

shrimp   _____

Circle the words that you would find between the guide words on each of these dictionary pages.

1. cactus/cavalry   106

(canister)	cast
caught	camel
capital	cedar
cage	cat
cable	cake

2. ferry/figure   273

final	few
feud	fiber
fright	fidget
fiddle	fever
fluid	fifth

3. quack/rally   602

quiz	rabbit
raid	quota
race	ranch
rake	rack
radar	queen

Many words have more than one definition, or meaning. A dictionary often gives several meanings for a word. Each different meaning is numbered. Some dictionaries even give sentences or phrases to show the different meanings.

Read each dictionary entry. Then read the sentences. Find the best meaning for the underlined word in each sentence. Write the number of the meaning on the line next to the sentence.

coach (kōch) *n.* **1** a large, closed carriage drawn by horses, with the driver's seat outside. *See the picture.* ★**2** a railroad car with seats for passengers. **3** a bus. **4** a class of seats on an airplane that are less expensive than those in the first-class section. **5** a person who teaches and trains students, athletes, singers, etc. [a football *coach*].

land (land) *n.* **1** the solid part of the earth's surface [by *land* or by sea]. **2** a country, region, etc. [a distant *land;* one's native *land*]. **3** ground or soil [high *land;* fertile *land*]. **4** ground thought of as property.

lock[1] (läk) *n.* **1** a device for fastening a door, safe, etc. by means of a bolt. A lock can usually be opened only by a special key, etc. **2** an enclosed part of a canal, river, etc. with gates at each end.

___4___ 1. When we fly to Chicago, we always go coach.

_____ 2. Our coach has us practice every day after school.

_____ 3. An air-conditioned motor coach will take us to the city.

_____ 4. The queen was driven to the palace in her coach.

_____ 5. Train passengers ride in a coach, not a caboose.

_____ 6. My family has owned farm land in the West for years.

_____ 7. The caravan is traveling to a strange and foreign land.

_____ 8. Earth is made up of water and land.

_____ 9. Land in a desert is very dry and arid.

_____ 10. An ocean-going vessel just entered the lock.

_____ 11. Carla always puts a lock on her bicycle.

Read the group of words in each box. Decide if you need to use the first, second, or third letter to put the words in alphabetical order. Then write the words in alphabetical order on the lines.

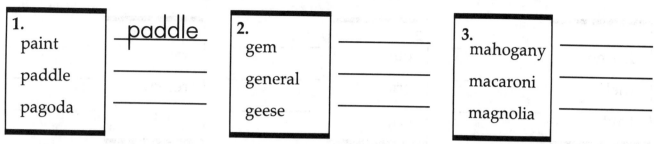

1.
paint   paddle

paddle   _____

pagoda   _____

2.
gem   _____

general   _____

geese   _____

3.
mahogany   _____

macaroni   _____

magnolia   _____

Read the words below. The read the guide words in each box. Write the words that you would find between the guide words on each of these dictionary pages.

mouth	skeleton	much	have	movie	hat
sky	haul	hawk	skirt	muffin	skate

1. hasty/head   336

haul   _____

_____   _____

2. mouse/mule   480

_____   _____

_____   _____

3. sizzle/slice   693

_____   _____

_____   _____

Read each dictionary entry. Then read the sentences. Find the best meaning for the underlined word in each sentence. Write the number of the meaning on the line next to each sentence.

pe·ri·od (pir'ē əd) *n.* **1** the time that goes by during which something goes on, a cycle is repeated, etc. [the medieval *period*; a *period* of hot weather]. **2** any of the portions of time into which a game, a school day, etc. is divided.

foot (foot) *n.* **1** the end part of the leg, on which a person or animal stands or moves. **2** the lowest part; base or bottom [the *foot* of a page; the *foot* of a mountain]. **3** the part farthest from the head or beginning [the *foot* of a bed; the *foot* of the line].

___2___ **1.** Students always like their recess <u>period</u>.

_____ **2.** Crops grew poorly during the dry <u>period</u> in 1988.

_____ **3.** Leave the package at the <u>foot</u> of the stairs.

_____ **4.** When Bertha fell, she twisted her ankle and broke her <u>foot</u>.

Read the group of words in each box. Decide if you need to use the
first, second, or third letter to put the words in alphabetical order.
Then write the words in alphabetical order on the lines.

1.		2.		3.	
frozen	_____	our	_____	ray	_____
fuel	_____	oriole	_____	receipt	_____
fruit	_____	organ	_____	reach	_____

Read the words below. Then read the guide words in each box. Write
the words that you would find between the guide words on each of
these dictionary pages.

fudge	fugitive	ornate	ounce	rebel	raven
ostrich	razor	fry	real	frown	ornament

1. frost/fun 297	2. ore/out 516	3. rattle/red 618
_____ _____	_____ _____	_____ _____
_____ _____	_____ _____	_____ _____

Read each dictionary entry. Then read the sentences. Find the best
meaning for the underlined word in each sentence. Write the number
of the meaning on the line next to each sentence.

club (klub) *n.*   **1** a heavy wooden stick, used as a weapon.
2 any stick made for some special purpose [a golf *club*].   **3**
the mark ♣, used on a black suit of playing cards; also, a card
of this suit.   **4** a group of people who meet together for plea-
sure or for some special purpose [a bridge *club*; an athletic
club].   **5** the building or place where they meet.

meet[1] (mēt) *v.*   **1** come upon; come face to face with [We *met*
two friends walking down the street.]   **2** to be introduced to
[I *met* you at a party.]   **3** to become acquainted [Have you
two *met*?]   **4** to be present at the arrival of [Please *meet* the
bus.]   **5** to keep an appointment with [I'll *meet* you at noon.]

_____ **1.** The lost hunter had a wooden <u>club</u> for protection.

_____ **2.** Our music <u>club</u> is giving a concert today.

_____ **3.** Harry will <u>meet</u> you at 3 P.M. as planned.

_____ **4.** Come to my party and you'll <u>meet</u> my cousin from Ohio.